DENTISTS:

AN ENDANGERED SPECIES

Dr. Paul Homoly

A survival guide for fee-for-service care

DENTISTS:
AN ENDANGERED SPECIES

Dr. Paul Homoly

A
survival
guide
for
fee-for-
service
care

KNOVA
PRESS

Charlotte
North
Carolina

First printing 1996

ISBN 0-9650639-0-9

LCCN 96-75060

Book design by gary hixson.
Set in Berling and Franklin Gothic Demi.

ATTENTION CORPORATIONS, UNIVERSITIES, COLLEGES, AND PROFESSIONAL ORGANIZATIONS: Quantity discounts are available on bulk purchases of this book for educational or training purposes. Special books or book excerpts can also be created to fit specific needs. For information, please contact Knōva Press, 500-H Clanton Rd., Charlotte, NC 28217 or call (704) 527-6600.

*This book is dedicated to my dental patients
who have been my constant teachers of the lessons
of practice and personal development.*

Contents

Between Selling Our Services and Saving Our Profession

In this first chapter we'll discover:

- *Is managed care the predator of fee-for-service dentistry?*
- *Identifying the major threats to dentistry*
- *The origin of preserving fee-for-service dentistry: case presentation*

Let's begin the process of preserving fee-for-service dentistry by clearing the air of what is really happening in dentistry. Are the insurance companies responsible for all our problems, or are there many other factors negatively affecting us that have nothing to do with insurance companies?

The second chapter asks some tough questions about preserving fee-for-service care:

- *Why is there a wide gap in dentistry between what we know and what we do?*
- *How can patients make informed decisions about today's high-tech dentistry when dentists have yesterday's communication skills?*
- *What are the two greatest barriers to implementing reconstructive dentistry?*

The case presentation process offers a powerful opportunity to overcome the barriers in the mind of the patient and yourself. An important step in solving fee-for-service issues is believing we can.

Contents

Understanding the Nature of the Beast

The fifth chapter details the critical factor of value. Value, an unexpected positive experience, gives patients more than their money's worth and creates the sense your office goes the "extra mile." Want to begin practicing outside the dental insurance and managed care industry? This chapter shows:

- *Unearthing your patients' concerns about money*
- *How unexpected positive experiences for the patient can tame the beast of reconstructive care*
- *Why value kills the appetite for insurance pretreatment estimates*

No practitioner has ever built a reconstructive practice by relying on dental insurance. Instead, they have done it by differentiating themselves in the mind of the patient, enabling the patient to choose their recommendation over that of the insurance company.

Don't Argue with Mother Nature

Chapter six describes how to follow through on determining the patient's budget for dental care introduced in chapter five. The key principle illustrated is to determine the budget before treatment is recommended. Only that portion of treatment that fits within the budget is offered. Treatment that falls outside the budget is completed in subsequent years. This chapter provides sample dialogs to guide you when discussing the annual dental budget along with:

- *How to make patients angry: quote high fees without knowing what they can afford*
- *Why to avoid the snares of patient financing*
- *Patient education can be like swimming upstream—it's easier when you go with the flow*

Money is at the heart of most fee-for-service issues. This chapter teaches us to stay within the financial comfort zone of the patients. Affordability combined with value create solid reasons for patients to accept fee-for-service dentistry.

Our next chapter details the value of the case discussion letter as a positioning tool for the practice. The case discussion letter is described in detail as are ideas for its implementation. Here are the highlights of this chapter.

- *The anatomy and physiology of the case discussion letter*
- *Reproducing case discussion letters*
- *More ways to differentiate yourself and create solid reasons for patients to accept fee-for-service dentistry.*

If you want to be positioned as unique in the minds of your patients, you must provide value beyond their expectations. The case discussion letter is a personal communication from you and creates a powerful environment for fee-for-service care to prosper.

Chapter eight shows how to structure informed consent as an important internal marketing tool and give the patient the most thorough understanding of the benefits, risks and alternatives to care. Nine specific issues of informed consent are discussed as well as how to implement financial contracts into the consent appointment. This chapter illustrates:

- *The preoperative appointment—your best weapon against medical/legal scavengers*
- *How to preserve your rights in a hostile litigious environment*
- *How to create the most complete dental record any plaintiff's attorney has ever seen*

Medical/legal issues are important in the business environment of the 1990s. Malpractice lawsuits provide the strongest incentives against advancement of our clinical skills and depletes the satisfaction with our careers.

Contents

Contents

This final chapter is about the mental preparation needed for practicing reconstructive dentistry. Like athletic competitions, visualizations along with healthy self-esteem, pride and an attitude of abundance prepare us for the rigors of providing excellent dental care. Preserving fee-for-service dentistry means, above all, preserving the fee-for-service dentist. *This chapter demonstrates:*

- *Why high self-esteem and an attitude of abundance are prerequisites for case acceptance*
- *The illusion of private practice*
- *How to provide unconditional value*

Whether or not your patients accept your treatment plans in a fee-for-service environment depends on your willingness to provide unconditional value. Patients will accept your care if they perceive you are uniquely qualified.

Acknowledgments

I guess writing your first book can be like treating your first patient—when you look back on the experience you realize how much others have helped. Tamara Easter, my marketing manager for seven years, has shouldered the weight all of the normal but unacceptable crises that accompany running a business and writing a book. My first thanks go to Tamara for her unconditional support and sense of humor.

Virginia McCullough, Barbara Lockman, gary hixson, and Marilyn Ross helped shape the manuscript into an easy-to-read book. They guided the process and allowed me to do what I do best. It's their work that has given this book its polish and style.

Along the way to completing this book, several people within the profession of dentistry offered great advice: Dr. Mark Davis, Dr. Bill Wathen, Dr. Stanley Allen, Dr. Jay Crawford, Dr. Wayne Jarvis, Dr. Carl Misch, Dr. Benson Clarke, Dr. Charles English, Dr. Burt Melton, Dr. Dennis Smiler, Dr. Jack Hahn, Dr. Don Masters, Bob Salvin, Linda Miles, and Tim Breiding.

And, of course, I'd like to thank my family—my wife Carolyn for being a great listener when I needed her support and my two children Adam and Kristen for staying out of trouble!

Thank you everyone for your advice and support. And I promise next time it will be easier!

The Missing Link

Between Selling Our Services and Saving Our Profession

In this first chapter we'll discover:

- Is managed care the predator of fee-for-service dentistry?
- Identifying the major threats to dentistry
- The origin of preserving fee-for-service dentistry: case presentation

Let's begin the process of preserving fee-for-service dentistry by clearing the air of what is really happening in dentistry. Are the insurance companies responsible for all our problems, or are there many other factors negatively affecting us that have nothing to do with insurance companies?

"Preserving fee-for-service dentistry" has become the battle cry in dentistry today. Informal groups gather in dim hallways at dental society meetings whispering about their opposition to managed care plans. Every journal in dentistry has taken careful aim at managed care issues, making sure not to ricochet into the wrong side of the anti-trust issues. Our top clinicians and industry leaders regularly speak of the perils of managed care and are champions of a "call to arms." United we stand, divided we fall they cry, shaming their colleagues who are managed care providers. Preserving fee-for-service dentistry is the dental industry issue *du jour*. Managed care and the dental insurance industry giants are this era's villains—or so it seems.

The facts about managed care don't support all the rhetoric about it as the culprit in the demise of fee-for-service dentistry. According to the January 1995 *ADA News* citing a study done in 1994, "two-thirds of U.S. dental practices remain strictly fee-for-service. Just eight percent of patients in U.S. dental practices are enrolled in managed care programs. And less than four percent of dental practices say half or more of their patients are enrolled in managed care."

The question I'd have you ask is this: If only eight percent of the patients served in 1994 were enrolled in managed care, how much could that possibly contribute to the fall of fee-for-service dentistry? Even if the managed care plan paid the dentist provider nothing for the dentistry done on its member, the loss of profit is far less than the loss in profit due to other factors unrelated to managed care.

For example, a dentist makes a decision to build a new facility and equips it with all the bells and whistles the dental equipment industry has to offer. After the dust has settled, the dentist has increased fixed expenses and debt, but has made no fundamental changes in the capacity to produce or collect. Predictably, net income goes down, stress goes up, and the quality of life erodes. Preserving fee-for-service dentistry for this dentist and thousands of others has nothing to do with managed care. It has everything to do with managing him or herself.

Or how about the dentist who acts as a "hired gun" expert witness for the plaintiff in a malicious malpractice lawsuit against you? Did you know there are thousands of dentists who, for a fee, will be glad to look for the holes in your defense and cheerfully testify against you? How does this behavior contribute to preserving fee-for-service dentistry? What does it have to do with managed care issues?

Or what does preserving fee-for-service dentistry mean to the dental team members, laboratory technicians, and dental suppliers? Do they adjust their performance in the best interests of the practice of dentistry—or just to themselves? Does the managed care issue affect day-to-day staff management so crucial to success?

My examples could continue. The point is there are many more issues that affect preserving fee-for-service dentistry that far outweigh the current influence of managed care. Escalating overhead, greater competition for dental dollars from outside of dentistry, the ever increasing complexity of dental practice management, the growing ugliness of dental/legal problems, occupational stress and isolation, and the difficulty of practice transitions have a far greater impact than managed care has had during its entire history. Add to these issues the fact that as practitioners age, our productive capacity decreases. If the entire managed care industry vanished tomorrow, the greatest factors affecting the quality of life of dentists and fee-for-service dentistry will remain.

I am not naive about the negative impact managed care has had in some areas and in some practices. Nor am I blind to the slow but steady advance managed care is making into our industry. But neither am I persuaded by the dentists who haven't kept their clinical skills current, don't study and use team building concepts, haven't improved their communication skills, and haven't marketed their practices—then say managed care is ruining their lives. Let's not shift the burden of making our practices prosper off of us and onto the shoulders of managed care.

It's true that managed care, OSHA, the IRS, and the legal system can make our lives more difficult. That's the way life is. But life also offers us a choice—a choice to adapt ourselves and thrive, not just survive, in the real world of normal but unacceptable regulatory and competitive business pressures.

This book is about adapting ourselves and thriving in the practice of dentistry. It's based on many things: my twenty years in private practice, ten years as a dental practice consultant, the collective experience of thousands of dentists, and an appreciation and awareness of real world facts about what makes a dental practice work or not work.

Preserving fee-for-service dentistry is important to me partly because it is about our relationships with the dental insurance industry. I've been a long-time skeptic of the true value of dental insurance as it relates to the doctor/patient relationship. In twenty years of practice on only rare occasions did I accept insurance assignment of benefits or file pretreatment estimates. Dental insurance is part of the relationship patients have with their employers and the insurance company. It is not between the patient and me. Preserving fee-for-service dentistry is about much more than our relationship with the insurance industry. Here's a definition of preserving fee-for-service dentistry:

> Dentists working together to create an environment where we can express our talents in private practice for the greatest benefit for the patient, the community, the profession, and ourselves.

It is not about creating protectionistic, anti-dental insurance industry laws. That is not going to happen. Preserving fee-for-service dentistry is about advancing our individual talents to create an environment where our best efforts collectively can do the most patients the greatest amount of good. I see preserving fee-for-service dentistry first solved on an individual basis. Then individuals who have created an optimal environment for their practices cooperate with other like-minded dentists to bring models of success to the profession. Dental politicians and other industry leaders who have not solved the fee-for-service problems in their own offices are hardly in a position to solve them for the profession.

I believe in taking personal responsibility to create the change and growth I want in my life. My individual talents and successes combined with yours—and aimed in the right direction (the needs of the patient, the community, the profession, then ourselves)—will create the right environment if we persist. Ultimately, if we are to create and then preserve the environment where our patients can thrive, we must first thrive.

Dentists—An Endangered Species is about the single most important topic that influences our success individually and our ability to preserve dentistry collectively. It's about managing that elusive exchange between you and your patient called case presentation. The link between our ability to "sell" our services and "save" our profession is clear. Too often it's been the missing link. When it is missing it offers no benefit to your patient, the community, the profession, or to you. Although there are many challenges in preserving fee-for-service dentistry, having your patients to say "yes" to treatment recommendations is the first challenge. Without this, all other fee-for-service issues are moot.

In this book I'll discuss case presentation for the more difficult and expensive levels of reconstructive dentistry. The principles used to present reconstructive dentistry can be used to present the full spectrum of dental care from pedodontics to full dentures. Keep in mind the real challenges upon us as you read. Your success in case presentation takes you only halfway to meeting the challenges of preserving fee-for-service dentistry. Compound your success by helping other dentists become successful so collectively, we can make dentistry a better place for our patients, our community, our profession, and ourselves.

Fossil Fuel
for Thought

The second chapter asks some tough questions about preserving fee-for-service care:

- Why is there a wide gap in dentistry between what we know and what we do?
- How can patients make informed decisions about today's high-tech dentistry when dentists have yesterday's communication skills?
- What are the two greatest barriers to implementing reconstructive dentistry?

The case presentation process offers a powerful opportunity to overcome the barriers in the mind of the patient and yourself. An important step in solving fee-for-service issues is believing we can.

Think about something for a moment. If you had to choose the single greatest obstacle to implementing reconstructive dentistry in your practice, what would it be? If you were to make a list of the most common frustrations you experience on a day-to-day basis, what would they include? Are these frustrations and obstacles related to the clinical components or to the business components of your practice? If you're like me and the hundreds of dentists I've know over the last 20 years, our greatest sources of frustration and obstacles are business-related.

I've practiced advanced restorative dentistry for the last 15 years. As a trainer and consultant I've taught thousands of hours of continuing education programs and have been a practice management consultant since 1986. As a practitioner and consultant, I've found that the most common frustration dentists share is the fact that training and technology enable us to produce far greater clinical results than many of our patients will allow us to do. It's as if we're all dressed up with no place to go.

There is a gap in dentistry between what we know and what we do. There are many reasons for this, the primary one being that clinical advances and technological breakthroughs have evolved past our ability to sell.

Clinical and technological advances come with a price. The price becomes a major barrier to the patient, unless dentists learn how to communicate the benefits of these advances. In short, we have created an appetite in ourselves and in our patients, but we haven't learned how to satisfy it or how to ask for the order.

Look at the facts. Prior to the industry-wide acceptance of large-scale cosmetic- and implant-related treatment plans, the average general practitioner rarely created treatment plans for cases exceeding $2,000 to $4,500. If a patient was diagnosed with advanced periodontal disease or total edentulism, dentures were the treatment of choice.

Today there are many alternatives to dentures and cosmetic alternatives that were not widely available before 1989. The average general practitioner now has access to and knowledge of techniques and referral options that can restore the partially and fully edentulous patient with far better restorations than full or partial dentures. However, the treatment fee quadruples. Where there was once a straightforward conversation about fees and dental insurance, there is now a major financial decision, which for some patients may represent a substantial portion of their savings and earnings.

High-tech dentistry is making its impact. CAD CAM machines that mill out porcelain inlays and crowns, digital radiography, intraoral video, computer-based records and chart systems, lasers, and CD-ROM all are at the cutting edge of what is sure to be an escalation of high-tech breakthroughs that will steamroll into the next decade. Like clinical advances, a high-tech world brings a price tag that adds fuel to the higher fee fires burning in every office wanting to practice on the cutting edge.

Clinical and technological advances are accelerating. Dentists are lined up for continuing education to stay abreast of new advances. Dentists' desks are smothered with journals touting all the new stuff. Ultimately, the deciding factor of where and how far clinical advances and technology will lead us will be determined by the answer to this question: Who will pay for it?

Dentists are learning they can't pay for it. Overhead expenses related to implementing new technology are growing out of control, causing many dentists to suffer economically and making it tough to sustain their practices.

Dental insurance policies aren't going to pay for it; dental insurance has never made a meaningful contribution to reconstructive care. In fact, dental insurance has been a deterrent to implementing clinical advances. By creating its euphemisms of "prior authorizations" and "usual and customary fees," dental insurance confuses, misleads, and limits its users and providers into thinking there is such a thing as a "dental benefits plan"—one of dentistry's best oxymorons.

Managed care plan providers will be the last ones to pay for it. At this writing, managed care contracts are calling for a 20 to 30 percent reduction of fees. A dental practice cannot flourish and embrace new technology by giving away all its profits. Still, there are dentists who are trying to make managed care work for them. In many ways, they are like confused sailors jockeying for position on the deck of the *Titanic*.

Who will pay for clinical and technological advances? The patient. There is no other way. The contemporary practice of fee-for-service reconstructive dentistry bears more resemblance to a hardware store than to a hospital. There are no HMOs or insurance plans that are going to pick up the check for dental reconstructive care. The dentist/patient relationship has more in common with a retail cash-and-carry style of doing business than it has with the physician/hospital/insurance company trinity. There is no one to pick up the tab for reconstructive care other than the patient.

Like it or not, the only way a dentist is going to implement today's technology and clinical advances is to learn how to sell them. Unfortunately, most dentists are attempting to sell today's technology with yesterday's (or the last decade's) sales techniques.

Case presentation for routine general dentistry differs from case presentation for reconstructive dentistry just as much as today's technology differs from that of a decade ago. The fees are much higher, stretching the patient's financial comfort zone. This is the obvious difference a higher fee makes.

What is not so obvious is that a higher fee stretches the financial comfort zone of the doctor and staff as well. Many of us in dentistry have yet to come to grips with presenting treatment plans that may be beyond *our* ability to pay. (Chapter 10 addresses this issue.)

Reconstructive case presentations differ from those of lower-fee general dentistry in that the consequences of failure are greater. Do you want to be responsible for a multi-unit cosmetic restoration of the anterior teeth with four quadrants of implant-supported posterior restorations for the remainder of the patient's life? When offering general dentistry, it's easy to be confident that your single-unit crowns and operative dentistry will work over the long term. Who guarantees that reconstructive dentistry will endure? Fear of failure is as much a barrier in the dentist's mind as it is in the patient's. (Chapter 8 tackles the tough issues of replacing existing dentistry—your own and that of other dentists.)

The differences between reconstructive and general care continue in light of patients' expectations. Patients impose a higher expectation on reconstructive dentistry than on general care. Part of this attitude is fee-related. But many patients also want so much to have a comfortable and attractive mouth, they create their own reality. They hear what they want to hear and often see their reconstructive dentist as a savior bringing them to the proverbial promised land. Less seasoned dentists buy into this illusion. Patients' high expectations brought on by the high fee and the illusion that the dentist can save them places greater demands on case presentation for reconstructive dentistry in the areas of informed consent and integrity. (Chapters 8, 9, 10, 12, and 13 offer support in these areas.)

Higher fees, greater consequences of failure, and exaggerated expectations are the offspring of reconstructive dentistry. All are brought to us by the "miracles" of modern dentistry. I'm sure our technology was designed with the intention of making our lives better. But has it? Many of us practice with a bitter frustration. The technology that brings a greater quality of life to our patients can offer the opposite to us.

This book addresses a problem at the heart of this frustration: selling the technology we have spent our professional careers learning. The barriers we must overcome in order to sell reconstructive care are similar to barriers faced in other careers. Teachers, salespeople, and athletes, for example, all confront barriers that block growth.

During the 1994 Winter Olympics in Lillehammer, Norway, a Norwegian skier named Stein Lisa Haddenstadt was competing for the gold medal in women's freestyle skiing. For the previous five years, she had been second in the world, but never first. Her coaches and fellow skiers knew that Stein Lisa was a world class competitor, but somehow, a barrier to winning the world championships and the Olympic gold medal was always there.

Convinced the barrier to her championships was in her mind, Stein Lisa decided to attack it in a symbolic way. CBS Sports produced a feature story on her and aired it two days before the gold medal event. She decided to try skydiving, convinced that if she could force herself to jump out of an airplane, she could win the gold medal. Stein Lisa believed that jumping out of the plane would symbolically break the barrier in her mind to being world champion.

The feature showed Stein Lisa's teammates cheering her on as she approached the small Cessna jump plane. She and her skydiving instructor buckled their bodies together; he wore the chute, she didn't. The camera showed Stein Lisa and her instructor shimmy onto the narrow jump platform, 10,000 feet above the Norwegian landscape. They pushed the spar away and floated to the surface.

The crew and reporters gathered as they approached the ground. "Why did you do this?" one reporter asked. With a wide grin Stein Lisa replied, "In order for me to win the gold medal, I must first break the barriers in my mind."

Two days later, Stein Lisa Haddenstadt climbed to the top of the gold medal platform in front of 40,000 cheering Norwegians. She had indeed succeeded.

Like winning an Olympic gold medal, getting case acceptance for reconstructive dentistry demands that we break through some long-standing barriers in our own minds as well as in the minds of our patients. So strap on that parachute and let's proceed.

BARRIERS IN THE PATIENT'S MIND

Unfortunately, the strongest barriers in the minds of dental patients have been put there by dentists. Practitioners who approach dentistry with well-meaning, tooth-by-tooth solutions to dental health crises unwittingly strengthen patients' resolve to resist, or at least mistrust, suggestions for further treatment.

Research indicates that lost time in treatment, costs, inconvenience, and fear of pain are the most significant barriers to dental care—fairly large obstacles in anybody's book. How they came to figure so prominently in patients' minds is evident in the following scenario.

She's a fairly typical candidate for rehabilitation—a married woman between 45 and 65 years of age, a high school graduate who's also attended some college—and she's ready for a change. More than likely she's in your office as a result of a significant event in her life.

Perhaps she was embarrassed at a luncheon when she bit into the French bread and broke off a corner of her front tooth. She may be in a great deal of pain. Perhaps she's just been divorced or widowed. Any number of life-changing events can precipitate a dental visit. When this patient enters your office, she doesn't come alone. She drags along an accumulation of past dental experiences as real and cumbersome as a sack of wet sand.

Perhaps, when she was in her teens, some dentist looked at her mouth and said, "You have a problem—cavities. And I'll sell you the solution—fillings." She and her parents agreed to fix the problem with fillings.

A decade later, another dentist observed, "Your problem is cracked filings. But I'll sell you the solution—crowns." So she got crowns.

A decade later, a dentist said, "You have a problem with gum disease. The solution is periodontal treatment." She agreed to treatment, but not without wondering when her teeth would stop being a problem.

Yet, another decade went by and a dentist looked in her mouth and reported, "Your problem is severe bone loss and loose and missing teeth. My solution is full or partial dentures." With great reluctance, she accepted dentures.

You guessed it. Ten years later she faced another dentist who quickly identified her problem. "Your partial denture has rocked out your remaining teeth. The solution for you is dental implants." When she heard the fee, she hit the roof. And who could blame her?

Most candidates for rehabilitative dentistry have heard the same story for years: "You have the problem. I'll sell you the solution."

If you want to be perceived as being different from these other dentists, you must behave differently. Yet, most dentists sound remarkably similar when making treatment recommendations. When we talk about implants, we mention available bone and the process of osseointegration. When we discuss restorative dentistry, we bring up occlusion and crowns. In conferences on cosmetic dentistry, we expound on the porcelain and contours. It all sounds the same to patients.

If you're skeptical, try tape recording some of your case presentations and ask several colleagues to do the same. Then compare the tapes. Although individual verbal styles may differ, the underlying message to patients is the same. The greatest barrier in the mind of the patient to reconstructive dentistry is the victimizing message they have heard all their life: "You have the problem. I'll sell you the solution."

BARRIERS IN THE MIND OF THE DENTIST
Just as patients have been conditioned by the problem-solution message, dentists have built mind barriers after

years of hearing patients say, "I can't afford it." It doesn't take long for us to stop offering reconstructive dentistry and go back to piecemeal solutions just to end the rejection. It's easier on the ego and much less stressful to stay within the annual limitations of dental insurance coverage and not to rock the boat.

Back in the late 1970s and early 1980s, I attended various two- and three-day seminars on the concept of complete dentistry. I finished all levels of the Pankey Institute by the mid-1980s. I considered my early training in restorative dentistry excellent and would have done it all over again. My early teachers inspired me and I thank them.

When I would return from one of those seminars, I'd come back filled with the "holy spirit" of complete dentistry. I'd take full-mouth records on all my new patients. I'd make seven vertical bitewings, multiple periapical radiographs, study models, face bows, intraoral photographs, blood pressures, and full periodontal charting. I'd chart initial contact in centric relation and palpate muscles of mastication. I'd seat the patient in my consultation area and preach to them the importance of complete dental care and reappoint them for a consultation. I'd duplicate my study models, send one set to the lab and have a complete full contour diagnostic wax up done and steam clean my articulators. I'd have an awesome collection of diagnostic charting; intraoral photographs; plus bitewing, periapical, TMJ, panoral and, in some cases, CAT scan films. There would also be before and after photographs of other patients, and an array of commercially prepared visual aids that demonstrated everything from periodontal pockets to subperiosteal implants. I had and used it all.

I'd say to the patient, "In order for you to fully appreciate and understand my recommendations for care, it's important that you understand how you got this way to begin with." Then I would digress into descriptions of the relationships between plaque, occlusion, parafunction, oral habits, diet, prevention, and regular dental visits and their effect on the soft and hard tissues, nutrition and overall dental, plus mental and physical health.

Following this introduction, I'd go into a tooth-by-tooth description of what I was going to do and why. I'd use supporting diagnostic tools to "prove" my points and proudly display my diagnostic wax ups to show their final result.

Sometimes 45 minutes to an hour would slip away. Outside the consultation area door, my staff would wonder if we had died. I'd get lost in my rhetoric, supporting and demonstrating my unwavering faith to the concept of complete dentistry. At times I'd be oblivious to my schedule and incoming patients would stack up like nervous airplanes anxious to land.

After I completed my exhausting presentation, the patient would often look at me through glazed eyes and ask, "Doc, this sounds—uhm—really interesting, but tell me one thing. How much is all this going to cost?"

That question would always irritate me. I learned during my hundreds of hours of continuing education that fees should not be a deterrent to complete dentistry. To this day I still remember the aphorisms of the teachers of complete dentistry: "If you're a quality dentist, there will not be enough time in the day to treat all the patients who'll want your care," and "Quality dentistry sells itself." I believed all of it and never built my case presentation around the budget of the patient. I took a fundamentalist approach to dentistry and believed there was only one "right way" to do things.

Asking me about cost cheapened my mission of tooth salvation. I'd think, "How can they ask about cost? Don't they know or understand what a gift excellent dental care is? How can they be so ungrateful?"

But still, "How much is all this going to cost?" became a predictable and inevitable prologue to my tooth salvation sermon.

I'd say, "Well, Mr. Borchert, the total fee for your case is $15,000; it's what I'd do to my own mouth or to my brother's mouth if we had your dental disease."

The patient would flinch then ask, "What did you just say? Did you say it costs $1,500?"

"No, Mr. Borchert, I said $15,000."

And as he repeated the words "$15,000," he'd look at me like he was looking into the sun.

"What? I had no idea it was going to be this expensive! What makes it so expensive?"

At this point, I'd go back to the features of my treatment recommendations, all the while having this feeling I was falling into a bottomless black hole. While I was groping for the right words to persuade my patient into seeing his dental health the way I wanted him to see it, I would begin to notice aggressive and negative body language coming from what was once an open, accepting person. Unaffected by the new "gospel according to Homoly," my unbelieving patient would stand and say, "You know Doc, let me go home and think about this. I'll call you."

And like the taillights of an old car I just sold, I'd watch one of my sheep leave my flock, never to be seen again.

That's when I'd feel the heat—the heat that starts just above your stomach in the area where you can get your wind knocked out. This heat would creep into my chest, shortening my breath and weakening my pulse. Soon the heat would tighten my throat, leak out of the collar of my shirt, and settle on my face like moist, thick swamp gas. My staff would look at their feet and hide as I'd retreat from the consult area. They did not want to share the unthinkable reality and shame with me, the reality and shame that being my best was not good enough.

I'd bounce back though. I'd think, "Hey it's the patient's problem. He's the one with the low dental I.Q. I'll get the next one." And when the next new patient would come into our cathedral of dental care, we'd hit him or her with all the trimmings—study models, radiographs, and duplicated models. I'd sit each one down and preach home care, occlusion, and excellence. I'd go through a tooth-by-tooth lecture of how I was going to save the patient from the sins of poor dental health. I'd occasionally give them a dose of, "I won't start any permanent tooth replacement until you can demonstrate to us that you are going to take care of your mouth. If you don't, you'll end up with a horrible disfiguring dental disease." I thought a touch of fire and brimstone might push the patient over the edge.

Well, I was right about one thing: it did push them, not over the edge but out the door. Yes, there were times that patients saw the light and completed care with us. But most of them, when they heard the fee, would squint, flinch, swallow, then walk.

Then, one day as we were getting ready to do a new patient examination and my assistant, Lisa, reached for the alginate trays, I said, "Lisa, we won't need the models this time." She gave me an odd, quick little glance; she knew something was going to change.

"Then I guess we won't be needing any of this," Lisa said as she turned her back, gave a barely noticeable sigh, and put up the bite registration materials and face bow.

She was right. Things did change during our new patient procedures. No more study models. Bitewings and panoral radiographs only. No more long lectures. I'd finish the examination, sit the patients up, and tell them then and there what they needed.

"You have a couple of teeth missing and I see some decay. Let's take care of the decay and get you to the hygienist. We'll see what your insurance will pay to get the missing teeth replaced. How does that sound?"

"Okay, you're the doctor. Here's my insurance form. Can I get some free toothpaste for my kids?"

The concept of complete dentistry began to die, one patient at a time. Why invest all the time and effort into treatment planning for these people, when almost all of them tell me they can't afford it?

Patients refusing complete dentistry based on cost was never a major consideration during my continuing education. My teachers seemed to rise above it. Some would almost dismiss questions relating to selling techniques or marketing with more aphorisms: "If you take care of your patients, everything else will take care of itself."

I thought I had understood—offer the best, work like hell, maintain the highest standards, stay in balance. Did I miss something through it all? I began to experience self-doubt. Maybe I didn't "get it." Maybe I wasn't part of the complete dentists club. Maybe I only knew part of the secret handshake to complete dentistry. I obviously needed something more. I needed the secret stuff they had but I didn't.

It had seemed so easy. The teachings were simple: Know your work. Apply your skills. Stay on the path. Success is a journey. Now I was up against a wall. No one had told me about the wall. You know which wall I'm talking about. It's the one we slam into after we get a running start into our careers. We go along and everything seems to be going our way, then we reach this wall and all the aphorisms, cliches, and philosophies bounce off it like BBs against an iceberg. Soon I began to suspect the skills that got me to the wall would not get me over it.

The wall in my mind had been built by patients who would look at me like they were squinting into the sun after I'd quote their fee. The objection, "I just can't afford it," began to build a wall in my mind one brick at a time. It was a big red cinder block onto which they'd trowel gray mortar that would stay soft and moist, anticipating the next patient's brick. Brick by brick, patient by patient, the wall would rise in my mind. After a half decade of "I just can't afford it," the wall became so high I couldn't see over it. And as my most recent patient fled my practice numbed by the expense of it all, she picked up an imaginary can of white spray paint, shook the can to awaken me with the click of the ball bearing, and sprayed, "I can't afford it" on the red brick wall in my mind. A kind of dental graffiti reminded me I didn't have the magic necessary for complete dentistry. The words "I can't afford it" seemed to mock my training and commitment to excellence.

When patients refuse comprehensive treatment plans, we tend to view it as both professional and personal rejection. No one likes rejection. To avoid this distinctly unpleasant feeling, we play it safe and avoid offering comprehensive plans that often carry a hefty fee. In short, we give up on complete dentistry and settle for halfway solutions that are more saleable.

Most patients would like to say "yes" to our recommendations for care. They just need help overcoming the mental barriers we have helped put in place. The "I can't afford it" message feeds our fear of rejection, which leads us to offer halfway treatment plans and more dental problems. This fosters the "You've got the problem, I'll sell you the solution," gambit, which results in "I can't afford it."

Somehow, somewhere, someone has to be first to get off the merry-go-round. We and our patients both want the same thing but we're too busy helping each other to *not* get it.

CONTESTS IN DENTISTRY

I learned early in life that there are some contests you just can't win. I came to this revelation in athletic duels with my older brother, Guy. A terrific natural athlete, Guy played professional football for the Cleveland Browns and AAA baseball for the San Francisco Giants. When we were in high school, Guy would take me out to Butterfield Park behind our house in suburban Chicago and pitch to me from a Little League pitching mound.

I could never hit the ball very well, because I had a weak right eye and wore thick glasses in those days. Guy, in his mercy, pitched to me with a tennis ball instead of a hard league ball. Those pitches would come streaking by my ear so fast it was like trying to hit an aspirin. To this day, I have never won a game of baseball against my brother. The only way for me to keep from losing was to never start the contest.

The same attitude can be applied to a dental practice. The dental health care process is peppered with contests—challenges of will, disputes, competition, and resistance to our way of thinking—involving doctors, patients, and staff. Practice management courses teach us how to manage these contests so the results are to our advantage.

Contests often start as surprises—"I didn't know my payment was due today."—or as unmet expectations— "Why are my new crowns so yellow?" Hassles over accounts receivable, appointment cancellations, or unmotivated employees can be won or lost, depending on your skill and experience as a manager.

There are some contests in dentistry, however, you can never win. The only way to keep from losing is to not start the contest. Chief among them is selling dentistry to patients before they are ready to accept it. If you start the contest, and patients refuse specific treatment plans, you lose. If they accept treatment because you used persuasion and charisma to push them into it, you will most certainly lose at some point in the relationship. These are the very patients who will sue you over complications, will do their best not to pay you, won't keep their recall appointments, will not refer to you, and, ultimately, will not like or trust you. You lose again.

What dentistry needs is a "no-contest" playing field. The natural, most obvious time to set the stage for a no-contest relationship is during the case presentation process, when you can prevent the contest from ever getting started. This is the time to begin to scale those barriers of the mind.

Throughout this book, be aware to keep in mind that these concepts of selling reconstructive care have worked for me and many of my clients. Temper this information with what you know currently works for you. I'm not telling you what to do. I'm telling you what my clients and I do and why we do it. Take our collective experiences, and put your own spin on them to make them work for you. Case presentation techniques are much like golf lessons. Adapt your natural talents to the techniques that have worked for so many others.

Revealing Choices

Patient Natural Selection

This chapter introduces a concept called the lifetime strategy for dental health. This chapter demonstrates several things:

- The choices your patients make will guide the evolution of your practice
- The Lifetime Strategy for Dental Health—a good choice for you and your patients
- In the right environment, most patients will make healthy decisions

The best weapon we have in the battle of preserving fee-for-service care is comprehensive treatment plans for our patients. After patients learn to appreciate a complete lifetime approach to their dental health, many of them will see the built-in limitations of their insurance and managed care programs.

The no-contest case presentation is a process for offering patients a different, more comprehensive style of dentistry. It's not a single appointment, nor is it a slick sales tool used to "close the deal" with patients. Far from a gimmick, the no-contest case presentation is a process designed and proven to prevent confrontations and re-move mental barriers to recommendations for a lifetime approach to personal dental care.

Don't be mislead by the term, however. This in no way implies no skill. On the contrary, effectively conducting a no-contest method of case presentation requires time, desire, and skill.

The process itself has six steps that flow together as a system. Here are the six steps and the chapters in which they are explained:

1. The initial examination—Chapter 3
2. The diagnostic appointment—Chapter 5
3. The case review—Chapter 6
4. The case discussion—Chapter 6
5. The review of findings letter—Chapter 7
6. The preoperative appointment—Chapter 8

This process is not necessarily six appointments. De-pending on the readiness of an individual patient, the no-contest case presentation process can be accom-plished in as few as three appointments. At other times it may take more. Whether it takes three, four, five, or six appointments, what's important is the chronological order of the six steps—always do step one before two, two before three, etc. The sequence is more important than the duration of the process.

The method of case presentation begins with the initial interview and exam. The clinical objectives of any ini-tial dental appointment are fairly clear and straightforward. During this first visit you review patients' medical and dental histories, conduct oral examinations, take radiographs, and present your findings to patients. Equally important, however, are the management objectives of the first appointment, because you must establish yourself in patients' minds as someone uniquely qualified to meet their needs. To succeed, your approach and behavior must be noticeably different from all other previous practitioners—those dentists who unwittingly set themselves up in the role of opponent in a no-win contest of wills.

You can set the no-contest tone early by resisting the temptation to make treatment recommendations at the initial appointment. Instead, offer a choice between immediate fix-the-chief-complaint care and a lifetime strategy for dental health. Make a clear distinction between these two choices, and you'll be immediately and pleasantly surprised at the results.

The choices your patients make guide the evolution of your practice. If your patients are making poor dental health care choices, it will negatively affect the environment of your practice—your attitude, your staff's attitude, the quality of care, and quality patient referrals. It's in everyone's best interest that you intervene in the random evolution of your patient base. Create an environment in your practice that offers two clear paths for practice growth; fix-the-chief-complaint style of care or a lifetime strategy for dental health. The environment within your practice guides its evolutionary path—poor choices lead to negative environments which lead to more poor choices. You are in full control of the environment within your practice. You control it by offering patients the right choices. And in the right environment, most patients will make healthy decisions.

Consider the case of Mrs. Leonard. "Mrs. Leonard," you say, "I can see why you are bothered by that broken tooth. We can fix that right away and be done with it, or we can include repairing your tooth as part of a lifetime strategy for your personal dental health. Which would you prefer?"

You have just offered your patient something she didn't expect—a choice between tooth dentistry and complete dentistry.

By offering this choice, you probably have begun distinguishing yourself from all previous tooth-oriented practitioners in her dental history—and you did it without a word of criticism or opinion about past dental work. Carving out a unique niche in the patient's mind is a crucial step to overcoming barriers.

Your response to patients at this initial meeting also requires sensitivity and choice on your part. Know when to play the lifetime strategy card and when to hold it. If a patient's chief complaint is causing pain, infection, or obvious cosmetic or phonetic problems, assume it needs immediate attention and move quickly to correct it. Avoid offering a lifetime dental strategy when patients are distressed. Present the choice of a lifetime strategy for dental health when patients are comfortable. For most, it will be a totally new concept.

Remember that a lifetime strategy necessitates a broad overview and detailed planning. Don't tip your hand now by suggesting specific treatments. During the initial visit, recommendations for treatment other than to satisfy a compelling need simply invite contests. In fact, they invite the worst possible contests—those you cannot possibly win. They ask patients to purchase dentistry before they are ready to accept it.

The initial appointment is paradoxical. Patients want to find out if they are in the right place to get their teeth fixed, but when they are offered treatment recommendations too soon, all they really hear is, "You've got a problem. I'll sell you the solution." In trying to discover what they want, dental patients often drive themselves further from it.

DON'T PLAY VERBAL VOLLEYBALL

Timing is everything. By bringing up the technical aspects of reconstructive dentistry (numbers of crowns, root canals, bridges, and implants) too early in the doctor/patient relationship, you risk starting a verbal volleyball game you can seldom win.

Watch how the game is played with Mrs. Leonard.

You serve by saying, "Yes, I can help you with that loose lower denture. Implants are safe and effective and have helped thousands of people just like you regain their confidence, appearance, speech, and self-esteem."

Mrs. Leonard returns your serve and continues the contest by asking, "What exactly are implants?"

You skillfully handle this return and put the ball back in her court when you answer, "An implant is a manmade tooth root inserted into the bone in the position once held by your natural tooth." This is a technically correct response, but watch out. You're already setting yourself up for defeat.

Your opponent—oops—patient, makes a cautious volley. "How many of these implants will I need and how do you put them in?"

Your return has pinpoint accuracy. "Mrs. Leonard, you'll need five implants inserted into the symphysis of your mandible. The surgery is performed right here in the office, and I can assure you a high level of safety and comfort throughout the operation." You are on your home court, feeling confident and in control. You know you have the skill and experience necessary to do the job.

Then it happens. Mrs. Leonard fires back a topspin overhand shot. "How do you know implants will work for me?"

You race to return the volley. "Well, there are no guarantees, of course, but statistics show excellent long-term survival rates."

Again, she drives you deep into the back court. "How much is all this going to cost?"

You barely get the ball back over the net as you reply, "Costs can vary depending on many factors. It's expensive, but it will be well worth your investment." Suddenly, your legs feel like rubber.

Sensing your stress, she rips one hard across the court, "How much will my insurance pay?"

You dive for the shot and with confused effort reply, "I'm sorry to say insurance pays very little, but maybe we can work out payments."

And with one seamless, powerful leap, Mrs. Leonard spikes her response with such force it's impossible to return. She finishes you off with, "I had no idea this would be so expensive. I'm going to have to think about it."

She takes her ball and goes home. You lose. In fact, you both lose.

As I discovered when trying to play baseball with my brother, there are some contests you can never win. It's best not to even start them.

Use the consultation phase of the initial dental exam to introduce the no-contest case presentation. Instead of discussing particular treatments, offer patients the option of a lifetime strategy for dental health that is free of entangling, specific, and technical recommendations. If you don't play the game, there can be no contest.

A good way to explain the idea to patients is by analogy. Let's try it with Mrs. Leonard.

You say, "If I'm planning to retire when I'm 62 years old, my accountant will advise me about certain things I need to start doing right now—today—to make sure that happens. Developing a lifetime strategy for dental health is a lot like financial planning."

Here Mrs. Leonard will undoubtedly nod. Even if she has not adequately prepared for her own financial future, she understands the concept and knows its value.

"If you want good dental health at age 62, Mrs. Leonard, there are certain things we need to start doing today." Your offer now gives her an opportunity to take charge of a significant area in her future affecting both her health and appearance.

No matter how well you present the idea of a lifetime strategy for dental care, most patients will still look for a way to engage you in a contest, usually by asking for an immediate technical recommendation. They may hear "lifetime," but they're still thinking "today."

Resist the urge to enter the conflict. Instead of leaping into a description of the features and benefits of your technical solutions, offer patients an opportunity to join with you in a well-planned strategy for complete dental health. You may further suggest more in-depth studies including X-rays, photographs, and models, stressing that you'll need time to give the case adequate study before making any specific recommendations.

I like to add, "Mrs. Leonard, let me study your case so well I'll know it by heart." Knowing it by heart has been a powerful tool for me in case presentation. The patient will hear the phrase "know it by heart" several times during the treatment planning phase. And the payoff for knowing it by heart comes when I actually present care to her. (More about this later.)

The emphasis of this conversation needs to be on *planning* care, not providing care. As we all know, the cases that go best are the ones that were planned the best. Don't be lured into a no-win contest with patients simply because they are anxious for treatment.

DARE TO BE DIFFERENT

It won't take long for patients to discover that you provide dentistry from a different perspective. You aren't trying to sell them solutions. You are offering them a plan. In fact, you've gone out of your way not to recommend specific care solutions. Consequently, some of those barriers in the mind begin to crumble.

Other barriers are harder to overcome. It's understandable patients will always be concerned with the cost of dentistry. Most will want to know the total price right away. In the no-contest case presentation scenario, avoid quoting dollar amounts for specific treatments. Direct your answers, instead, toward the planning process. Go ahead and tell patients the approximate cost of the planning process, and mention that dental insurance usually covers it. After all, you want your patients to be informed partners in the process. Otherwise, it's just another contest.

When a patient persists in asking for specific treatment recommendations, use your experience to not answer the question. You read correctly. Use your experience to not provide technical recommendations for care. We are so accustomed to using our experience to answer patients' requests that it almost seems unnatural not to. But beware, a contest lies just beneath the surface of the most innocent sounding questions.

For example, Mrs. Leonard may ask, "Before I go, just tell me one thing. How long will my treatment take?" Using my experience in order to not answer the question, my response is framed within the lifetime strategy for care. "Mrs. Leonard, the time it takes to complete your care will depend on what we do. If I've learned one thing in my 15 years of doing cases just like yours, it is to not make any specific recommendations before I've had a chance to really study your case. I'll be sure to address this concern soon after I've taken the time to learn what would be best for you." This approach has been very effective in reinforcing the planning phase of care and avoiding the contests.

Still, a few patients will demand that you play. "Look, I'm a very busy person," they'll say. "I don't have time to spend in a dentist's office trying to find out what I need. Can't you just give me a general idea what I need and how much it will cost?"

The contest you didn't want in the first place is now at its peak. The next point wins. Patients are now begging you to tell them everything they don't want to hear. ("You have the problem. I'll sell you the solution.") In the past I've looked these patients straight in the eye and said, "I'd estimate that a case like yours will cost $10,000 [always overestimate ballpark fees] and will take me eight months to complete. If that is within your comfort zone, Mrs. Leonard, we can begin soon. Is this appropriate for you?"

Game over. If patients say "yes," you can proceed through the planning process. If they gasp, are visibly pale, and squeak "no," suggest to them they go through the planning process to get to all their answers.

Always keep the door open, however, by stressing that when they're ready to develop a lifetime strategy for dental health, you'll be there to assist. Take care of their chief complaint and keep them on recall.

Fortunately, this all-or-nothing approach is rarely needed. Most patients are pleased that you want to take the time to plan their care adequately before making recommendations. They appreciate, though rarely realize, that the old barriers in the mind are weakening. For once, they don't have to enter an adversarial contest with a dentist to get the kind of care and attention they desire.

Following are some sample dialogues (examination and post-examination discussions) at the initial appointment. One dialogue outlines the conversation with a patient who accepts the concept of a lifetime strategy, the other with a patient who does not.

Dr. Homoly: Hello Mrs. Leonard. I'm Dr. Paul Homoly. Welcome to our office. How can I help you today?

Mrs. Leonard: I'm pleased to meet you, Dr. Homoly, and I hope you can help me with my problem. I've been to a couple of different dentists and am a little confused. You see I've worn this lower partial denture for many years now. Recently, I've noticed that the teeth it's hooked to are beginning to get loose, and my gums are always sore. I went to my daughter's dentist and he made X-rays and molds and talked about three or four different plans. Frankly, I'm a little confused. A friend of mine said she had a cousin who came here and said I should talk to you. What do you think is the best way for me to get comfortable again with my teeth?

Dr. Homoly: I'm sorry to hear that you are uncomfortable, Mrs. Leonard. Let me take a good look in your mouth before I make any specific recommendation. Let me ask you, though, how is your general health? You look really healthy.

Mrs. Leonard: Yes, I am. My last physical went well. My blood pressure is a little high, but we're watching it.

Dr. Homoly: Let me introduce you to my assistant, Jeannie. She'll seat you, and I'll be with you in a minute.

Mrs. Leonard: Thank you. Oh, before we go back, can you tell me how much all of this is going to cost?

Dr. Homoly: The examination costs $85, Mrs. Leonard, and it will take us about an hour. Is that all right with you?

Mrs. Leonard: It is, but what I meant was, how much will fixing my lower teeth cost?

Dr. Homoly: Let me take a look first, and before I do anything to your teeth, we'll discuss your budget and what's appropriate for you. Is that okay?

Mrs. Leonard: That's fine.

We have completed the examination and are seated in the consultation area. Mrs. Leonard's chart lies closed on the table. The X-ray viewer is off.

Dr. Homoly: I hope that examination was comfortable for you.

Mrs. Leonard: It was fine. Your assistant was really nice. She reminded me of my daughter.

Dr. Homoly: How many children do you have?

Mrs. Leonard: We have two, Amy and Megan. Amy is the one who told me I should come here.

Dr. Homoly: I have two kids also—Adam and Kristen. They're both successfully masquerading as college students. Adam goes to Appalachian State and Kristen goes to Lees McRae College.

Mrs. Leonard: Both of our girls are married now, so my husband and I have an empty house, but we enjoy it when they come to visit.

Dr. Homoly: I see a lot of good things about your mouth. Your overall bone levels look good and the relationship between your jaws is fine. I can see why your gums are sore. Your partial denture is loose and has rubbed raw spots on the gums.

Mrs. Leonard: What can you do about that?

Dr. Homoly: There are two ways for us to approach this problem. We can go back to the chair right now, and I can adjust your partial and put a quick reline in it. That will take care of the discomfort and will make things feel better, but it won't help tighten up those loose teeth. The other approach is to take a more comprehensive look at things and develop for you a lifetime strategy for dental health. Which approach would you like me to take?

Mrs. Leonard: What do you mean by a lifetime strategy for dental health? What is that?

Dr. Homoly: A lifetime strategy is like retirement planning. When I told my accountant I wanted to retire by age 62, he told me that in order to do that, there were things I needed to start doing today. If you want great dental health at age 62, 72, or 92, there are things we need to start doing today.

Mrs. Leonard: What do we need to do today, Dr. Homoly?

Dr. Homoly: You actually have already started what you need to do. This examination is the first step in putting together a lifetime strategy. I recommend that I call your previous dentist and see what his plans were.

Mrs. Leonard: He had several plans, and like I said, I was a little confused about what he thought was best. He seemed irritated when I said I wanted a second opinion. Should I have him send my X-rays here?

Dr. Homoly: Let me call him and see how we can best help you. I suggest we assemble the necessary diagnostic materials in order to study your case so I'll know it by heart. Next appointment we'll get the records we need and continue the planning process.

Mrs. Leonard: Can you give me some idea about how you'd fix my lower teeth? My previous dentist showed me some models and pictures and told me I might be able to have implants or something like that. Do you do that here?

Dr. Homoly: We do. But before I make any specific recommendation, let me plan your case. After I believe I know it well enough, I'll get into all the details and costs. One thing I've learned in the last 15 years of treating cases just like yours is that some of the most important time we spend together is time spent planning the right way to do things. Is that all right with you?

Mrs. Leonard: How much will my insurance pay for this? We're on a fixed income and my husband and I need to watch our budget.

Dr. Homoly: Your insurance will pay for almost all of the diagnostic work. I estimate that will be about $150 and your insurance will pay most of it. Let's get you scheduled for our next time together. After I've finished studying your case, I'll show you your lifetime strategy for dental health and discuss its costs. Would you like me to make any adjustment on your partial denture today?

Mrs. Leonard: That would be great if you would. How long will that take?

Dr. Homoly: I'll get Jeannie right now and we'll have you out of here in five minutes. I'll have Ginger, my office manager, make your next appointment with us.

Mrs. Leonard: Thank you.

Now, here's some sample dialogue where the patient does not accept our offer for a lifetime strategy.

Dr. Homoly: Hello, Mr. Crawford. I'm Dr. Paul Homoly. Welcome to our office. How can I help you today?

Mr. Crawford: I've been to a couple of dentists, and they all tell me something different. I just want a straight answer, you know what I mean? And I don't have a lot of time and money to throw at this problem. My partial is killing me. I've had it a couple of years and it's never been right. There are times when it seems okay but most of the time it isn't. I have to take it out to eat.

Dr. Homoly: I'm sorry to hear you are uncomfortable. Let me take a good look in your mouth before I make any specific recommendation. Let me ask you, how is your health?

Mr. Crawford: I'm healthy. I've outlived two doctors already.

Dr. Homoly: Let me introduce you to my assistant, Jeannie. She'll seat you and I'll be with you in a minute.

Mr. Crawford: Doc, are we gonna do something about this partial today?

Dr. Homoly: I'd like to. Let me take a look and I'll do what I can.

Mr. Crawford: Good. Sooner the better. Oh, by the way Doc, you're not going to take X-rays are you?

Dr. Homoly: I was planning to. Is that all right?

Mr. Crawford: Listen, Doc, I fix cars for a living. If a customer has a flat I don't check the spark plugs. You know what I mean? Can't we just fix this partial?

Dr. Homoly: Sure. Jeannie, take Mr. Crawford to operatory and set up for a partial adjustment. We'll fix his partial today and do his exam when he's ready.

We have completed adjusting Mr. Crawford's partial denture. It's an all-plastic mandibular flipper with wrought-wire clasps. It's been repaired in two areas and moves a quarter of an inch upon opening. Mr. Crawford is seated in the consultation area and his chart is on the table, closed.

Dr. Homoly: How does that partial feel now?

Mr. Crawford: Much better, Doc. Thanks. I'll let you know how it does when I chew. How much do I owe you?

Dr. Homoly: Let me tell you how it's going to feel when you chew. It's going to rock and move and probably break again. In fact, it might not even last the time it takes you to walk to your car. You fix cars for a living, Mr. Crawford. Your partial is like an old set of bald retread tires that have been patched and plugged. Have you ever told customers they're going to have to get new tires?

Mr. Crawford: Yeah, everyday.

Dr. Homoly: Well, you need new tires in your mouth. A new partial may be the answer, but it may not be. You come back to me when you're ready to get your teeth fixed and I'll put together a lifetime strategy for dental health for you. I'll put you in our recall system to make it easy for you to remember.

Mr. Crawford: What do you mean by a lifetime strategy for dental health? What is that?

Dr. Homoly: A lifetime strategy is like retirement planning. When I told my accountant I wanted to retire by age 62, he told me that in order to do that, there were things I needed to start doing today. If you want great dental health at age 62, 72, or 92, there are things we need to start doing.

Mr. Crawford: Like what?

Dr. Homoly: First, an examination. Then I'll call your previous dentist and see what her plans were. Before I make any recommendation, I need to look under the hood. Do you know what I mean?

Mr. Crawford: Okay. Next time we'll do the exam.

The management objective of the examination appointment is to introduce the concept of a lifetime strategy for dental care. We avoid getting into technical recommendations for care because they will lead us down the road to recommending treatment before the patient or the dentist is ready to proceed. Emphasize planning.

Emphasize "knowing their case by heart" before making any recommendations.

You'll be pleasantly surprised by the number of patients who will jump at the chance to have a lifetime strategy for their dental health. For patients who don't accept a lifetime strategy, take care of their chief complaint and keep them on recall. Then offer the lifetime strategy at subsequent appointments.

Offering the patient a choice between complete dentistry (the lifetime strategy for dental health) or "fix" the chief complaint only represented for me a major shift in thinking about my approach to clinical care. Prior to my shift, all patients were offered the same thing: complete care. Based on the training, cliches, and stories from my teachers, people would play ball. Quality sells. Unfortunately for me, it didn't. After I got my nerve up to discuss my problems with my dental colleagues, I discovered that my quality-oriented dentist friends had exactly the same problems. Many of them still do.

One day it dawned on me that I needed to do business with my patients on the terms they wanted, not those I wanted. I had the attitude "my way or the doorway," and many of my patients chose the latter. But I did not want to abandon the concepts of complete dentistry because it is the best clinical approach.

What evolved was a consumer-driven focus. It seemed odd at first, but ultimately it proved to be strikingly obvious. Why not just ask patients what approach to care they wanted? The question seemed easy. What was difficult was not being judgmental about their answer. Somehow I lost respect for patients who preferred to fix their chief complaint only and walk around with dental disease. And this loss of respect was communicated in my tone of voice and body language. People sense that they don't meet with your approval.

The single greatest area of growth I experienced as a dentist was the day I finally stopped judging my patients and accepted them and the choices they made about their dental health. Why make a contest out of it? Why fight reality? The day I stopped judging my patients was the same day I made the greatest advance in the quality of my care.

Consequently, my new patient examination became short and sweet. For most of my new patients I'd make a panoral radiograph only, no intraoral films at all. My clinical examination would be thorough, but I would hold off on the photographs, TMJ films, and study models. It became my experience that too many diagnostic steps during the first appointment inspired too many contests ("Why are you doing all these things?") and the examination fee rose to unacceptable levels for many patients, especially those looking to fix the chief complaint only. My examination would be thorough enough for me know the overall dental health of the patient but simple enough not to start contests with the patient.

My life as a dentist got easier once I abandoned the "my way or the doorway" approach to new patients. No longer were patients leaving my practice, never to be seen again. Instead, I began to build two levels of patients: those who were interested in a lifetime strategy for dental health (complete dentistry) and those who wanted to fix the chief complaint only. I stopped imposing my values on others and learned to cheerfully treat them at the level they preferred.

My full-time associate became responsible for most of the patients who chose to fix the chief complaint only. He was grateful for this and pleased to treat the patients. Often, the patients who would choose to fix the chief complaint only, would one day announce they were ready for complete care. (In Chapter 11, I'll discuss the importance of the associate within the reconstructive practice.)

The concept of complete dentistry worked best for me when my practice was open to all levels of preferred dental health. With judgment set aside, patients felt welcome, my staff was relieved of listening to me confess the sins of our patients, my associate thrived, and the ulcers that had been eating holes in my stomach went away.

The lifetime strategy for their dental health is a new concept to most patients. It's a way you can begin to differentiate yourself in their mind. It's a way you can begin to remove the mental barriers and provide a logical transition to the next step in the no-contest case presentation process: the diagnostic appointment.

Communication Survival Skills

The only way patients learn to appreciate the benefits of comprehensive fee-for-service care is through the communication skills of the dentist and his/her staff. Our dental education and most of continuing dental education totally ignores this topic. In chapter four we'll discuss:

- How all members of the dental team can thrive, not just survive, in the communication jungle
- The contrasts between the messages we say and the messages we send
- Why quality dentistry does not sell itself

Our profession is filled with highly trained dentists who possess the technical ability to provide rehabilitative care, but are stuck on a plateau of professional development because their patients won't accept their recommendations. Communication skills must be on par with technical skills.

Your communication style can literally make or break barriers in the mind. Your unique style may be the single most important—and controllable—key to achieving no-contest dentistry. While you're examining a patient with severe dental problems, can you visualize how that mouth will look when restored? I think most dentists who have practiced reconstructive dentistry would agree that they can see the final result before treatment begins. Being able to visualize the final result is the key to it. Patients have much more difficulty visualizing their final result. By practicing a few proven techniques, you'll be able to effectively transfer the picture in your mind to your patients so they can comprehend just how they'll look and feel after completing care. The greatest gift you can give your patients is the ability to see themselves as you see them.

The real art of dentistry doesn't lie in your technical skill, but in your ability to communicate with patients. Research has shown that between 50 and 60 percent of communication is visual, meaning while patients are listening to you, more than half of the message they receive comes not from what you're saying but from how you're saying it. Visual communicators include body language, physical appearance, gestures, hair, dress, and facial expression. The sound and tone of your voice contribute about 30 percent and your vocabulary another seven to 10 percent.

Unfortunately, the majority of dentists are most proficient in the area of least overall importance. We often rely on procedural, technical, and trade jargon to convey our message to patients rather than emphasizing visual and tonal qualities. Why? First of all, we tend to make case presentations to patients in the same way we were taught in dental school and in continuing education programs. In other words, we lecture, but we call it patient education.

Think about it. Clinical lectures are presented in slide or video format with a teacher at the front of the room standing in the dark, so it's impossible to see the individual's features or body language. To top it off, the instructor's tone of voice is modulated to sustain an hour-long monologue. We've spent decades in dark rooms, hypnotized by slides, and we have unconsciously patterned our communication style after that modeled by teachers. This approach may be sufficient for the simple transfer of clinical information, but it makes for lousy case presentations.

Our body language and tone of voice are effective when we are completely confident and comfortable. I often say, "When you know, it shows." And when we know, truly know, without a shadow of doubt, that we possess the skills to rehabilitate our patient's mouth, it shows. Our patients can see it in all the verbal and nonverbal signals we use to communicate: posture, hand gestures, facial expressions, and breathing. Patients pick up quickly on these cues. Since they read you like a book, make sure it's a book they like reading.

THE MESSAGE WE SAY AND THE MESSAGE WE SEND
There are two messages delivered when we speak: the message we say (the meaning of the words) and the message we send (the total interpretation and impact of the communication). As dentists, we have been trained

to focus on what we say. We have ignored, and in some instances have been encouraged to ignore, how we say it. But the fact is that the patient bases his or her decisions on how we say it. I am not aware of a single dental school in America that offers training for dentists on adding credibility and strength to their communication. What is even more alarming to me is that many dental societies do not offer continuing education credits for seminars on communication skills. Ask patients what they like (or dislike) about their dentist, and you'll hear answers that are partially or totally influenced by the communication style of the dentist.

Two major areas affect the message we send: the way we sound and the way we look. Too many of us ignore the cues our patients send to us about their preferred style of communication. Many of us make the mistake of following the Golden Rule: Do onto others as you would have them do unto you. How you would have a person communicate to you in no way represents how you should communicate to them!

For example, let's say you are an energetic, type A achiever. You prefer a direct, "get to the bottom line" style of conversation. ("Just the facts, Ma'am," as in the old *Dragnet* television series.) Your patient is a slow-talking, nervous, amiable woman whose dental problems are embarrassing and have caused her problems relating to her appearance, self-confidence, and intimacy. Following the Golden Rule, you would speak to her as you would have her speak to you. Wrong.

If you are the slow-talking, amiable, storytelling "good old boy" and your patient is Mr. Bottom Line who glances at his watch and checks his pager every two minutes, then you would need to change your style, too.

Your communication style should harmonize with your patient's style. Do you always speak quickly and get to the point with Mr. Bottom Line? Of course not. There will be times when a slower-paced, focused style is needed. But for the most part, Mr. Bottom Line will appreciate direct answers and a minimum of small talk. Do you always engage in long conversations and frequent sidebar family conversations with Mrs. Amiable? Of course not. But I can assure you someone in your practice will need to invest in giving Mrs. Amiable a good listening to. Become aware that different folks require different strokes.

Tone of voice can influence the message we send. High-pitched, nasal-sounding tones carry less authority than do lower tones. Breath control is important. When you are rushed, irritated, and behind in your schedule, your breathing rate increases and becomes more shallow. This raises your pitch and lowers your impact.

Eye contact is the most crucial element of appearance. Great eye contact is one of the most important elements of our communication. This fact should come not with any great surprise; all of us have heard that. But have you ever wondered why eye contact is so important? What is it about the eyes? What is it that we are looking at when we make eye contact?

Many researchers have shown that the eyes can't lie. That is, the eyes give predictable clues to the internal mental and emotional states. When we are lying our pupils constrict; when we are aroused and interested they dilate. Different eye contact styles send various messages. Darting eyes, looking left and then right, never making solid eye contact, can be distracting and irritating to the listener. Gazing, looking into space, not making eye contact at all gives a strong impression the speaker is totally uninterested and distant. Slow blinking, keeping your eyes closed for three to five seconds, sends a message that the speaker is totally aloof or completely disinterested and would prefer to be somewhere else.

The ability to make and hold appropriate eye contact (five-second intervals) sends a strong message of involvement, enthusiasm, and confidence. It's what patients want to perceive. Why make great eye contact? It's not just for you to look into your patients' eyes, but rather to give them the opportunity to look into yours. Let them see into you. Let them read your inner motives and emotions. Give them the answers to their questions: Is my dentist interested in me? Is she confident? Am I hearing the truth? Can I trust him? Does she like me? Your eyes will give them clues on the conscious and unconscious level to the fundamental questions people ask that affect their willingness to accept your treatment recommendations.

Make a video of yourself during case presentation (with the patient's permission), and notice where you and the patient look during your time together. I've had many experiences with my associates and clients, in which they focused their eye contact almost totally on the X-ray viewer, some visual aid, or a treatment planning form. Patients will look where we direct them. Direct them to look at you.

Effective doctor/patient communication depends on a willingness to display and convey your unique personality, not just raw information. Don't be fooled. It takes time and practice. Most of us have shunned adding visual and tonal characteristics to add strength to our communication out of fear of sounding like salespeople. We have been mislead into equating enthusiasm with manipulation.

Our misconceptions about communication are born out of widespread myths within the culture of dentistry. The biggest culprit may be the myth: "Quality dentistry sells itself." This notion and many others perpetuated by well-meaning clinicians have the same underlying theme: Technical quality is all you need to be successful in your practice. All of us want to believe these myths because they coincide beautifully with what we have been trained to do, which is to provide quality dentistry. We really want this and other myths to be true.

Unfortunately, they are not. Dentists who say, "Look at me. My clinical dentistry is good, and I'm remarkably successful," also know and practice effective sales techniques. Many dentists are so natural when they use visual and tonal characteristics to add conviction to their communication they don't even know they're doing it. Yet, they're still led to believe it's the quality of their work alone that inspires people to agree to their treatment recommendations.

Understand that there is nothing wrong or unethical about being enthusiastic about what you do as you break through this barrier in the mind. If you enjoy your work and believe it to be in your patients' best interests, do not hold back your genuine delight in being able to offer them something of value.

We use visual and tonal characteristics in all other types of communication, so don't drastically change gears when talking to patients. Most of our human language package—watching, listening, speaking, reading, and writing—relies on visual and tonal qualities. We narrow and dull our human experience and make ourselves dreadfully boring to be with if we don't enjoy these fundamentally human communication characteristics.

USING VISUAL AIDS

The most obvious way to add visual impact to your communication style is through the use of visual aids. But don't start dragging out the dog or hitching up the pony yet. In the hierarchy of communication value, the strongest visual aid you have is yourself. You contain the entire communication package. Use this resource to its greatest potential.

Your staff also has high visual value. Each member of your office staff sends a powerful visual message to patients through physical appearance, facial expression, and body language. Make sure your staff members are transmitting the message you want your patients to receive.

Your office facility, with its furnishings and surroundings, ranks high in the hierarchy of visual aid value. Although these items don't require verbal support, they offer very important cues to patients about your self-image and point of view. The appearance of your office plays a significant supporting role in the impact of communication. However, don't believe for a second that building a new office or redecorating an old one will make you a more interesting person or rescue a collapsing bottom line. In almost every instance, case acceptance problems stem from poor communication, not unattractive decor.

The next slot in the hierarchy of value is hand-held visual aids. Use these to illustrate the technical aspects of dentistry; they require verbal support and can be held or easily viewed by patients. Plastic models, before-and-after photos, implant-supported dentures, and partial dentures all invite the use of verbal skills.

Two-way communication is enhanced when patients can actually handle the visual aids as they ask questions and make comments. The value of this communication exchange depends on how well you handle it. Technically oriented visual aids can deepen a patient's understanding of the treatment process, or they can invite a contest too early in the doctor/patient relationship. Be careful in your timing when presenting a hand-held visual aid. Since it will inspire questions, remember that you want those questions asked only when patients are prepared to hear the answers.

The visual aids with the lowest value are those that have visual characteristics, but require no verbal support. These include printed items: brochures, letters, question-and-answer sheets, and other types of pamphlets. Their classification as a low-level visual aid is not intended to reduce their importance. But when patients take these items home, away from you and your office, you lose control over their impact because you're not there to add verbal support. Remember, few visual aids are exclusively visual; their support requires a verbal explanation. In other words, effective communication is a total package.

One common mistake is allowing a low-impact visual aid to overpower one with potentially greater impact. For example, most of us use a radiograph as a visual aid during a case presentation. When we place the radiograph on the viewer and turn on the bright light, our patients' visual focus is on that radiograph. Use these sparingly to illustrate a point quickly and simply. Don't compete with your own visual aid for eye contact with patients. Turn the viewer on only when you want to use it, make your point, and then turn it off. Keep in mind that eye contact with verbal support is the highest level communication tool we have.

Be careful about using before-and-after photographs, too. There is nothing wrong with using photos, because they are outstanding to illustrate the benefits of your care. Just be sure to remove the pictures and restore eye contact with patients before attempting to explain treatment. Otherwise, you'll be sending competing messages. There is a reason art galleries are quiet. It's to let the message of the art come through on its own. Allow your patients to receive the message from photographs before you regain eye contact and start talking.

Using visual aids effectively also requires flexibility. Don't assume that every patient wants to see visual examples of the care you intend to offer. Most individuals approach any discussion of dental treatment with a degree of fear or dread. Visual aids can sometimes increase that anxiety and often shock patients. Some patients even feel insulted or embarrassed viewing study models of their own teeth. It's best to ask patients if they want to see these aids. Most people will say yes. Those who prefer not to see visual examples are telling you that they relate better to the human elements of communication than to the technical aspects of dentistry.

CHANGING YOUR CASE PRESENTATION STYLE

How important are communication skills to the success of your practice? There is a direct link between the growth of your clinical skills and experience and your mastery of communication abilities. Delivering complex, rehabilitative dentistry requires far better communication skills than needed when providing routine operative dentistry. In fact, you will provide very little rehabilitative dentistry unless your communication skills are on a par with your clinical skills.

Our profession is filled with highly trained individuals who possess the technical ability to provide rehabilitative care, but who are stuck on a plateau of professional development because they can't seem to convince patients to accept treatment. These frustrated professionals often confuse a patient's unwillingness to pay with their own inability to effectively communicate the true benefits of care.

For a successful practice to grow, you must use effective, no-contest communication techniques to help patients accept care, in addition to the clinical expertise necessary to deliver that care. Changing your case presentation style also demands flexibility. Most candidates for rehabilitative dentistry, for example, are 45 to 60 years old and more sensitive to and selective about the kind of information they let influence them. Younger patients are generally more open and nonselective when filtering health care information. The content-intensive style may be effective when discussing routine crowns for a young adult, but it meets with far more skepticism from older patients facing complex treatment, especially if patients are more than 10 years older than you.

Consider all the variables and adjust your case presentation accordingly. Ignore the myths, and proceed with confidence and enthusiasm toward the goal of no-contest dentistry. You can't lose. And neither can your patients.

Diagnosis

Understanding the Nature
of the Beast

The fifth chapter details the critical factor of value. Value, an unexpected positive experience, gives patients more than their money's worth and creates the sense your office goes the "extra mile." Want to begin practicing outside the dental insurance and managed care industry? This chapter shows:

- Unearthing your patients' concerns about money
- How unexpected positive experiences for the patient can tame the beast of reconstructive care
- Why value kills the appetite for insurance pre-treatment estimates

No practitioner has ever built a reconstructive practice by relying on dental insurance. Instead, they have done it by differentiating themselves in the mind of the patient, enabling the patient to choose their recommendation over that of the insurance company.

As soon as you can, assemble the diagnostic information necessary to develop each patient's plan for a lifetime strategy of dental health. Be prepared to follow through quickly on the process you've established during the initial exam and consultation. If there's time and it's convenient for your patient, go ahead and assemble the diagnostic records following your conversation about the benefits of the lifetime strategy. If not, reschedule at the patient's earliest convenience. By starting quickly, you are stressing the importance of formulating a lifetime strategy and reinforcing the message that you care about each individual's needs.

The clinical objective of the diagnostic appointment is to assemble all diagnostic materials necessary for developing a lifetime dental health strategy. The diagnostic record can include full mouth radiographs, TMJ films, study models, face bow transfers, photographs, bite records, and periodontal charting.

The management objectives of the diagnostic appointment include: reinforcing the lifetime strategy concept, demonstrating the unique and valuable qualities of your practice, positioning staff and associates as cotherapists, introducing the concept of a dental budget, and getting a commitment for the next appointment, the case review.

REINFORCEMENT

If you find yourself repeating the lifetime strategy message over and over, that's good. Telling patients once about a concept that is new to them is rarely enough. Advertising and marketing research shows that people may need as many as six to eight repetitions before they can recall new concepts. Take every opportunity to re-inforce the message. For example, "Mrs. Leonard, we've made all these models and X-rays so I can properly plan your lifetime strategy for dental health."

Use the diagnostic appointment to showcase value within your practice. Value is a relationship between what a person gives—pays—for something and the rela-tive worth of what he or she receives in return. To demonstrate value to people, you give them what they perceive as more than their money's worth. Value is the unexpected positive experience that people will remem-ber long after they've forgotten which tooth you crowned.

For example, in January 1995, I presented a program in White Plains, New York. My flight landed late, and it was about midnight when I walked into the baggage claim area. Standing there to meet me was a man dressed in a chauffeur's uniform holding a sign with my name on it. He picked up my bags and walked me out to the stretch Lincoln Continental limousine. This car was so long that the driver was practically in the next time zone! Soft music played as we glided along. Snow had piled on the top rails of the split rail fences. We soon arrived at the Rye Town Hilton. By now it was 12:30, and I was almost asleep in the back seat.

The driver carried my bags in, and as I entered the ho-tel, I was greeted by the receptionist, whom I can only describe as an angel. She smiled at me as I approached the front desk. "Hello, Paul," she said. "We've been wait-ing for you." She handed me my room key. "You're all checked in. All you have to do is walk a few steps down that hall and your room is ready."

As I walked to my room I thought, "How did she know my name? How did she do that?" Of course—the limo driver. And how about that greeting: "We've been waiting for you." That was nice.

I've traveled often in my career, and I can't tell you how many times I've slid the key into the slot and opened the door into a pitch black hotel room, worrying that maybe this is the time the guy with the hook is standing behind the door. When I opened the door this time, a small colonial lamp beside the bed was on. I walked in and heard soft classical music playing from the clock radio. The bed was turned down with a gold-foiled chocolate placed on the pillow. "Mom?" I thought. "Are you here, Mom?"

What did it cost the hotel to have the chauffeur waiting for me at baggage claim? Very little. And what did it give to me? A lot, especially at 12:30 in the morning. That's value. What did it cost the hotel for the "angel" at the front desk to say, "We've been waiting for you"? Basically, it cost them nothing, but to me it was just what I needed to hear at the end of a very long day. That's value. And what did it cost for the light to be on in my room, for the music to be playing, and a chocolate to be waiting? It cost them very little, but it meant a lot to me. That's value.

Let me ask you something. In your dental practice, is the light on for your patients? Is there something special you do for your patients that gives them more than they expected? To what would they attach worth that would cost them or you very little? When you discover that, you discover value. One way to get patients to agree to your treatment recommendations is to demonstrate value before you recommend care.

Here are just a few things you can do to bring value to the doctor/patient relationship before you recommend care.

1. *Stay on time.* Do not keep patients, especially new patients, waiting. Begin and end each appointment on time. To help keep things running smoothly, reserve specific time slots in your weekly schedule for diagnostic appointments.

2. *Consider batching appointments.* Combine all initial and subsequent consultation appointments on Monday afternoons or Tuesday mornings. Perhaps making them the first appointments in the morning or immediately following lunch will work best for you. Avoid placing these sessions between prosthetic appointments or following long surgical procedures where you may lose control of time.

3. *Be prepared.* Send your new patient information packets to the patient's home so patients can fill out registration forms and health histories there. Be prepared to give great directions to your office over the telephone to those who need it. Print easy-to-read maps. Have a fax machine to send maps and other information easily.

4. *Be organized.* Have all your operatory materials ready. It's easy for patients to feel comfortable in a clean, well organized office where the doctor and staff look and sound like they know and like what they're doing. That's value. And as we continue through the case presentation process, I 'll emphasize areas where value can be added.

HOW YOUR STAFF CAN ADD VALUE

Use diagnostic appointments to position your staff and any associated dentists as members of the treatment team. Patients need reassurance that others involved in the lifetime strategy process share your personal concern for them and have comparable technical skills. It represents value to the patient when all team members present a consistent message.

Consider the following scenarios:

You've just completed study models on a patient, and you leave the room for a moment. Your patient uses this time to ask your dental assistant, "Why is the dentist doing all this stuff? How much do you think it will cost for me to get my front teeth capped?"

Or, you ask your associate to start endodontics on a tooth that became sore between the initial visit and the diagnostic appointment. After a pleasant visit, the patient asks your associate if implants are painful and whether hospitalization is required.

Or, on her way out of the office, your patient asks the receptionist if she can make payments because she's concerned about being able to afford care.

Each of these situations packs the potential for starting the contest in dentistry. To short-circuit the competition before it starts, make sure each team member knows the basis for the proper response. The basis is simply to repeat the importance of developing an overall strategy for a lifetime of dental health. If a staff member or associate doctor attempts to explain further or tries selling too early, the contest can begin and it will be up to you to deal with it. Educate your staff about your expectations.

THE TIMING OF PROVIDING VALUE

The timing of providing value can be strategically planned to coincide with the management objectives of the appointment. Remember, value creates a sense of worth. It's a differentiating characteristic to which we want the patient to respond. The response we want will depend on where the patient is within the dental care experience. For example, you can divide the dental care experience into three parts: before treatment is accepted, during treatment, and following treatment.

Valuable experiences are designed for the patient before treatment is accepted, thereby meeting the management objective of having the patient accept our treatment recommendations. Doesn't it make perfect sense to create a sense of value for the patient before you offer comprehensive care? What can you do to create this? Different things offer relative value to different people. Having a small business area with a local telephone line, fax machine, and desk would offer tremendous value to Mr. Bottom Line businessman but would go unnoticed to the retired women who boasts to you about her grandchildren. She'd find value in reception room chairs that are easy to get in and out of and pictures of your (staff) family in a practice photo album.

Rethink everything you have in your reception room and everything you send and say to the patient before offering treatment in terms of its value. When designing your new patient procedures, ask yourself this question: Does this procedure offer value to my target patient? You'll find yourself standing by your aquarium or mounted trophy fish and scratching your head as you wonder to whom these ornaments provide value. Providing value before treatment is recommended is fundamental to being perceived as being someone special to the patient.

Adding value before treatment recommendations has a profound affect on how the patient perceives the "value" of dental insurance. Our goal is to provide more value than the insurance company. Adding value in patient relations kills the appetite for insurance pretreatment estimates and other limits imposed by the insurance company. Adding value early in the patient relationship, before treatment is recommended, foreshadows the end result—more value for the patient. It's the expectation of future value that drives the present desire to accept care under your terms, not the insurance companies'.

Providing value during the treatment experience is something dentists as a group have done very well. The management objective of providing value during the treatment process increases patient confidence and enhances patient comfort, which leads to patient referrals. Good examples of adding value during the treatment process are pain-free dentistry, sedation, and staying on schedule.

One of my favorite avenues through which to add value during the treatment process is having doctors and staff with a good sense of humor. My goal was to make the practice of dentistry fun. Patients liked being with us, and they referred plenty of their friends. Humor doesn't come naturally for everyone, however. If you're not a humorous person, surround yourself with people who are. Our willingness and ability to see and enjoy the humor in life is at times the only antidote to the situations dentistry and life can bring to us.

Doctors often tell me they use high-tech dentistry to add value to the dentist/patient relationship. The new high-tech areas of computer-based tomography, CDI learning systems, photography, and charting systems sometimes offer more features than value from the patient's point of view. Don't make the assumption that installing new digital radiography will significantly add value. The same is true about intraoral cameras. Yes, intraoral cameras can show patients things they may not be able to otherwise see. But, don't camouflage the value of the technology by relying only on its features. The greatest value of intraoral images is not the "gee whiz" reaction you get when patients see the fractured filling in the back of their mouth. The greatest value lies in your ability to communicate that this technology will allow you to study their case when they are not in the dental office. This saves them time (value) and creates a heightened sense of therapeutic thoroughness (value). Additionally, intraoral photography provides a baseline of dental health that can be called on in the future if disease or an accident should occur. This is convenience (value) and safety (value).

Go beyond the features of the tooth and the image of the tooth when using high technology. Give patients the big picture of the value of technology. Intraoral images of a patient's teeth, digital radiology, computer-assisted voice activated charting systems, and other new high-tech dental equipment and procedures should be presented to patients from the perspective of value. Explain to patients how this technology saves them time, money, and inconvenience; creates a better end product; relieves discomfort; adds beauty; and otherwise gives them more than their money's worth. That's value.

To facilitate demonstrating value to patients, create a value inventory of all significant technology and develop a value statement that translates the features of the technology into the language of value to the patient. Make sure that each staff member and doctor knows the value statements for all technology available in the office.

Here's an example of a value statement for an intraoral camera.

"Mrs. Adams, this is a computer-assisted camera. I'll use it to make a picture of your mouth, which will allow me to study your case when you're not here. That saves you time and will add convenience to having your teeth fixed. Since these images will be saved, in the future, if there is any change in your dental health or if you are involved in an accident, we have a permanent record of your existing dental condition. This is very important in a lifetime strategy for dental health. Because these images are saved on the computer, there is no conventional photographic film or processing needed. This saves time and money, something we all could use a little more of."

Value statements are important for technology in nonclinical areas as well. For example, some patients would find value in having CDI educational programs in the reception area. Others may find value in having cable or network television available while they wait. Businesspeople love having a fax machine and business space available to them. In multicultural communities, where some patients or staff may have language barriers, having small pocket translators available is a great way to offer value.

Offering value following treatment is important for maintaining referral and recall systems. For many busy patients, the six-month recall appointment holds little value if they do not perceive they need it. The way to provide value following treatment is to understand what is valuable to the patient. The businessman, who has just completed a $15,000 reconstruction, may find the value in the recall appointment if you remind him that regular checkups will help preserve his investment (value) and correct any small problems before they become big, thereby saving him time and money (value). Just be sure you don't waste his time when he comes in for his appointments.

The grandmother who brags about her grandchildren and who has just completed a full mouth reconstruction will often value the relationships she has established in the office. The dental care is important to her, but the relationships are the "icing on the cake." Customize your recall notices with value statements that fit the value system of the patients.

Become aware of the importance of the timing of value. Patients will judge the quality of their dental care on the value they experience. Don't be shortsighted and assume patients will recognize the technical quality of your dentistry and translate that technical textbook quality into value. Most patients won't. They expect to get quality care. It's what they are paying for. Value is giving them what they don't pay for.

Timing is everything. Harmonize the events in your office so peak value experiences for the patient coincide with those times when patients are making decisions about accepting your health care recommendations, referring other patients, and maintaining their recall relationships with you. Value, the unexpected positive experience, can tame the beast of reconstructive care.

POWER TALK

A thorough diagnostic records process normally takes an hour or more, and it provides an excellent opportunity for you to practice one of the most effective skills you'll ever use in dentistry. The skill of power talk—the ability to communicate a message that is in total harmony with your management objectives. Capitalize on the luxury of having your patient's complete, undivided attention. It doesn't happen often in the real-world practice of dentistry.

Consider, for example, the process of positioning a patient for a panoral radiograph. You literally hold the patient's head in your hands and are as close as you'll ever be to having that individual's full attention. Power talk is a simple statement made at this point of patient focus: "Mrs. Leonard, we're going to take real good care of you here;" "Mr. Adams, you're in the right office to get your teeth fixed;" "Mrs. Campbell, we're glad you're here," or "Kristen, your teeth are going to be beautiful when we're finished."

A direct, sincere message at a point of focus is the essence of power talk. It supports your management objectives and ultimately helps patients break through the barriers in their minds. It represents value to your patients when they sense your practice is not like all the others.

Do you know what your staff members discuss with new patients when you're out of the room? Consider training your staff to use power talk. Power talk is not manipulation. It should occur as a natural part of a cheerful dialogue with patients, but it should be direct and focused. It's the message we want to give at the precise moment when patients are concentrating on what we're saying.

Dental assistants can use the bitewing radiograph appointment, for instance, as an opportunity to say more to patients than just "open wide" or "bite down please." Have them introduce other members of the team. "Mrs. Leonard, did you meet Jeanie? She's our other chairside assistant. Jeanie has been with this office for six years. She's terrific." Sensing harmony among the staff represents value to patients. Think about it. Would you want dentistry done on you when you sense the doctor and assistant don't get along?

Keeping staff members and associates playing on the same team requires thoughtful practice. Role play is an effective way to rehearse proper responses to common situations that occur during the various kinds of appointments. The goal is to keep your communications strategies in harmony with the objectives of each specific appointment.

WHERE THE RUBBER MEETS THE ROAD

The most important management objective of the diagnostic appointment is to introduce the concept of a dental budget. It is the pivotal determinant for the rate and sequencing of a lifetime strategy. You can move no further in developing a patient's lifetime strategy without determining that individual's budget.

You don't have to approach dental budgeting with fear and trepidation. Here's one way to introduce the concept:

"Mrs. Leonard, I'm going to study these models we've made so I'll know your case by heart. But one of the things I'm going to need to know before I can make certain decisions is what's appropriate for your budget. Have you thought about your budget?"

Notice, you don't ask, "What is your budget?" This question only pressures patients to respond with a dollar figure, which they may not be prepared or willing to offer. Ask instead if your patient has thought about a budget. By phrasing your question correctly, you give patients many more response options. Even though replies will vary with every patient, keep your response consistent. Always assure patients you'll do what is right for them.

Mrs. Leonard may say, "No, I haven't given much thought to a budget. I figured you'd tell me what's best for me and how much it will cost."

But Mr. Humbert might reply, "Yes, I have, and I really need to know how much my insurance will pay before I can go ahead with anything."

Miss Bamber could declare, "Yes, my budget is $200 a month and I can't go over that."

Your answer to each of them should be the same.

"I understand. We'll talk more about what is appropriate for your budget during our next appointment, and we'll be sure to do what's right for you."

The strategy behind this approach is to alter the case presentation sequence most patients have come to expect. Instead of offering treatment solutions with accompanying price tags, use the no-contest procedure to first determine a patient's budget, then offer treatment recommendations based on that budget.

Altering the traditional case presentation sequence is like agreeing to the rules before the contest starts. The rules we agree on are costs and treatment priorities. Because most patients never anticipate this reversed sequence, you need to be extremely clear and straightforward in your presentation. Let patients know what's coming so they won't be surprised or offended.

Make sure patients know that during the next appointment you will be talking about money. Budget conversations are much less awkward when all participants know exactly when they'll occur. Saving the patient from an awkward or embarrassing situation represents value.

By introducing the concept of a dental budget during the diagnostic appointment, you foreshadow a specific decision-making opportunity at the next scheduled visit. The initial mention of a budget should never be used as a high-pressure sales ploy. Don't push for specific figures; you'll only trigger the old contest reflex. By using no-contest strategies, you should see your treatment acceptance percentages soar.

In Chapter 4, I said we offer two messages when we speak: the one we say and the one we send. When we discuss budget, if we make darting eye contact, our voice has a hint of stress in it, or our body language is defensive, our patients will sense our discomfort and become uncomfortable and suspicious. On the other hand, if we establish and maintain good eye contact, speak with calmness and confidence, and maintain friendly posture, people will sense our genuineness and will come away with the feeling that we are aware of budget realities and plan to respect those realities. That's value.

It's been my experience with associates, clients, and personal relationships with dentists, that many dentists are uncomfortable quoting high fees for large reconstructive cases. There is no way your eye contact, tone of voice, and body language will exude confidence if you are not internally confident. You can't get the cart before the horse on this issue: You must be comfortable with and enjoy the process of discussing fees with patients to convey the appropriate message. In Chapter 10, I discuss some of the mental barriers we have with money—our own and our patients' funds. *We* have to get past the money issues before patients ever will.

DIFFUSING THE INSURANCE TIME BOMB

Whenever the concept of a budget is raised, patients automatically assume their dental insurance provides an adequate and secure safety net. Unfortunately, it's you who ends up walking the tightrope. You have to deal realistically with patients' assumptions about what insurance will cover without discouraging them or scaring them away. The fact is, traditional dental insurance packages pay a very small percentage of fees related to total reconstructive care.

It's a big mistake to let patients believe their insurance will cover a large portion of care. It's an even bigger mistake for you or your staff to assume it will. It is a very devaluing experience for the patient when you allow dental insurance issues to manipulate the doctor/patient relationship.

Disarm the insurance issue before it is raised as an objection to accepting care. Give each new patient a clearly worded explanation of your policy concerning dental insurance in the new patient package. One of the best ways to diffuse the insurance time bomb is to state your payment expectations up front. A realistic model to follow is to require one-third of the total fee to initiate care, one-third near mid-treatment, and one-third when treatment is complete.

File insurance after the final installment is paid. Put it in writing and let your new patients know the facts. The fact is that dental insurance provides only a minor amount of reimbursement for reconstructive care. If you rely on dental insurance as a sales tool for reconstructive dentistry, you'll never do much reconstructive care.

Volumes have already been written on "tricks" for dental insurance reimbursement by consultants who are

convinced they hold the magic formula for getting insurance companies to pay for reconstructive care. Frankly,
there are no tricks. Traditional dental insurance programs
have specific annual maximum limitations, and that's
that. Don't devalue the experience by raising patients'
hopes that insurance will pay for their care, only to tell
them later that it won't.

A statement that has worked for me goes like this.
"Mrs. Leonard, dental insurance is not like medical insurance. Medical insurance normally has a high
deductible but covers catastrophic loss. Dental insurance, on the other hand, has a low deductible, but does
not cover catastrophic loss. You have catastrophic dental loss, and it's been my experience that dental insurance
will pay only a small portion. Your dental insurance
will not help you, but I will."

Here's sample dialogue from the diagnostic appointment. Our patient is seated in the consultation area.
Study models, a full-mouth series of radiographs, intraoral
photographs, a centric relation bite registration, and a
face bow were all made.

Dr. Homoly: Mrs. Leonard, it looks like you got through that
appointment all right. The reason we did all of
that is so I have something to study when you're
not here. Next time, I should have a good idea of
the best way for us to go.

Mrs. Leonard: That's fine. I don't remember anyone taking pictures of my mouth before. Do you do that to all
your patients?

Dr. Homoly: Not all my patients, no. In your case, we're developing a lifetime strategy for dental health. These pictures will help me learn your case by heart.

Mrs. Leonard: I see. By the way I brought my insurance policy with me today. It says here you need to fill this out before any work will be paid for. Do you have any idea how much this will cost yet?

Dr. Homoly: I do, but let me say one thing about dental insurance. Dental insurance is not like medical insurance. Medical insurance normally has a high deductible but it covers catastrophic loss. My uncle Ernie had a bypass operation and his insurance paid for the whole thing. Dental insurance, on the other hand, has a low deductible, but doesn't cover catastrophic loss. You have catastrophic dental loss, and it's been my experience that dental insurance will pay only a small portion. Your dental insurance will not help you much, but I will.

Mrs. Leonard: I was afraid our insurance wouldn't do much for me.

Dr. Homoly: Let me study the models we've made, so I'll know your case by heart. But one of the things I'm going to need to know before I can make certain decisions is what's appropriate for your budget. Have you thought about your budget?

Mrs. Leonard: Yes we have. And that's why I've been asking about my insurance. Can we see how much they are going to pay before we start? That way my husband and I will have a better idea of what we'll have to pay out of our pocket.

Dr. Homoly: Talk to your husband about your budget and next time we'll make some decisions that are within your budget. Let me get Ginger to make your next appointment.

Mrs. Leonard: That will be fine.

Here's another dialogue. Remember Mr. Crawford, the auto mechanic, from Chapter 3? His partial denture broke and he threw it away. He's back and just completed his exam.

Dr. Homoly: Mr. Crawford, it looks like you got through that appointment all right. The reason we did all of that is so I have something to study when you're not here. Next time together I should have a good idea of the best way for us to go.

Mr. Crawford: Tell me, Doc, how much is all of this gonna cost?

Dr. Homoly: I don't know yet. In your case, we're developing a lifetime strategy for dental health. These pictures will help me learn your case by heart. I'll know what the costs will be after I've planned your care.

Mr. Crawford: I don't have any dental insurance. Will my health insurance pay for some of this?

Dr. Homoly: Probably not. Bring your booklet in with you next time, and we'll take a look. Let me study these models we've made, so I'll know your case by heart. But one of the things I'm going to need to know before I can make certain decisions is what's appropriate for your budget. Have you thought about your budget?

Mr. Crawford: That's why I've been asking about my insurance. I don't know how much these things cost. I know it's expensive like everything else these days. Doc, I don't have a budget. You tell me what I need and I'll tell you if I can afford it.

Dr. Homoly: That exactly what we'll do next time. We'll make some decisions that are within your budget. Let me get Ginger to make your next appointment.

Mr. Crawford: Let's make it soon.

The diagnostic records appointment continues the process of differentiating you in the mind of the patient. Most patients have never had a comprehensive diagnostic workup. Remember, in order to be perceived as being different from other dentists, you must act differently. Focus on providing value during the initial appointments before recommending care. Doesn't it make perfect sense to instill in the patient the value of your services before you offer reconstructive care?

Introducing the concept of budget is a critical part of the diagnostic appointment. It foreshadows the financial discussions that will follow, without getting into any specifics that may invite a contest. Being aware of and respecting patients' budgets provides value. In fact, both the initial examination and the diagnostics records appointments should be viewed by the doctor and the staff as opportunities to demonstrate value prior to any specific recommendations for reconstructive care. You break through the barriers in the mind of the patient with the impact of value.

Case Review and Discussion

Don't Argue with Mother Nature

Chapter six describes how to follow through on determining the patient's budget for dental care introduced in chapter five. The key principle illustrated is to determine the budget *before* treatment is recommended. Only that portion of treatment that fits within the budget is offered. Treatment that falls outside the budget is completed in subsequent years. This chapter provides sample dialogs to guide you when discussing the annual dental budget along with:

- How to make patients angry: quote high fees without knowing what they can afford
- Why to avoid the snares of patient financing
- Patient education can be like swimming upstream—it's easier when you go with the flow

Money is at the heart of most fee-for-service issues. This chapter teaches us to stay within the financial comfort zone of the patients. Affordability combined with value create solid reasons for patients to accept fee-for-service dentistry.

An absolute prerequisite to the budget-based case review appointment is to know the technical and financial aspects of the lifetime strategy. This means taking the time to create a treatment plan for your patients—and being able to present that plan with a clear understanding of its financial ramifications. The key here is to know their treatment plan so well, you'll know it by heart. Remember that phrase? You used it during the conversation immediately following the initial examination. Now it's time to put it to work.

Find a quiet place in your office to assemble what you consider the best treatment plan that you and your treatment team can provide. Your treatment team includes practitioners inside and outside your office. Assemble your plan without regard to fees. Don't let the barrier in your mind that whispers, "They can't afford this" affect your clinical judgment. Offer the best you know how to deliver. We'll cross the financial bridge a little later.

Fight the temptation of putting alternative treatment plans together. Alternative treatment plans are great in dental school to impress your instructors by showing your treatment planning range. Offering alternatives and letting the patients choose their treatment plan is horribly confusing to the individual and time-consuming for you. Be decisive. You decide what the approach should be.

Once that decision is made, now commit it to memory. Know the overall technical and financial requirements by quadrant or by arch, depending on the case. I cannot overemphasize the effect you'll have on patients when you're able to discuss in detail the technical and financial aspects of their case without ever losing eye contact.

No fumbling through records looking for X-rays. No embarrassing moments of using a calculator to add their fees in front of them. Know it by heart. When you know, it shows.

The clinical objective of the case review appointment is to review treatment recommendations; the management objective is to determine budget without allowing financial considerations to be an obstacle to treatment nor the only motivator.

Don't think of this appointment in terms of a traditional case presentation, in which you explain specific recommendations and assign a cost figure to each. Instead, describe your recommendations in the future tense and make them conditional on the patient's budget and time restrictions. This portion of the no-contest case presentation is the case review. After we have determined the budget, then we offer treatment that falls within the budget. This portion is the case discussion.

There's an important distinction between case review and case discussion. The case review is the process where we give the patient an overview of what is possible, contingent on their budget. Then, after we learn what the patient can afford, the case discussion is the specific recommendation for care that falls within that budget.

In traditional case presentation there usually is no distinction between what the patient needs and what they can afford. Why? Because in traditional case presentation we discover the budget *after* we offer care.

Here's a good example of working into the case review.

"Mrs. Leonard, the teeth missing in your lower jaw can be replaced with nonremovable teeth. How and when we could do that would depend on your budget and time schedule. Also, those upper front teeth that have large broken fillings in them can be made to look like new again with porcelain crowns. How and when we might treat them, again, depends on what makes sense for your budget."

Speaking in the future tense and tying treatment recommendations to patient's budgets communicates that you realize any decision about getting their teeth fixed is going to be substantially budget- and priority-driven. Such an approach allows patients to mentally move themselves from the dental chair to the driver's seat in determining the course of their own lifetime strategy for dental health.

SET A BUDGET EARLY

The next step may seem backwards as it flies in the face of long-cherished dental tradition, but it's essential in the no-contest approach. Once in the consultation area, direct conversation to the patient's budget *before* discussing details of treatment recommendations.

Why? Most patients are open to talking about their budget at this point in your relationship because they've already had three high-quality experiences in your office in which you have not tried to sell them anything. Remember our discussion about value in the previous chapter? Demonstrate value before you zero in on the budget. People are far more open if they believe you know what value is all about.

Patients are willing to discuss budget because you previewed the topic of a dental budget at the previous appointment and made it clear that financial considerations would be discussed during a case review. Since the conversation is not a surprise, patients will be grateful for your sensitivity to their financial status.

The true management objective here is to determine a budget *before* making any specific recommendations for treatment. Go ahead and ask the question, "Is there a budget that we need to stay within?" Don't be afraid to discuss precise dollar amounts; this may help to eliminate misunderstandings. The message you want to send your patients is this: "I have a good grasp of how best to serve you, but I'm hesitant to make specific recommendations until I know what financial commitment you're comfortable with and are willing to make."

After you've asked the budget question, stop talking and listen. Give patients time to think and prepare a response. Don't offer more information, justify your request, or even make small talk to fill the silence.

When patients respond with a specific dollar amount, respect it as the absolute budget. If it's greater or equal to the fee for the general lifetime strategy you've previously discussed, the pressure is now off. Patients no longer have to wonder what your care might cost, and you don't have to wonder if they can afford it. You can proceed directly to questions and preparations concerning care.

The discussion recommending care that is within the budget is called the case discussion. Keep in mind the distinction I described earlier. The case review occurs before you know the budget and the case discussion occurs after you know. Do not confuse the sequence of these two discussions. The case review gives an overview without specific recommendations. The case discussion is the specific recommendations within the budget. You can't recommend care within the budget if you don't know the budget.

If a stated budget is not adequate to complete the lifetime strategy for dental health, don't take up the contest at this point. Simply acknowledge without judgment that you understand what the budget is. Then, present to patients only those aspects of care that fit within their budget. Here's where knowing their case by heart really pays off. Without fumbling through their record and losing the eye contact that is so critical to communication, you can continue your presentation. This seamless flow from their budget to your recommendations for care shows you have done your homework. You know their case by heart. It represents value to patients when they realize their dentist is totally familiar with all aspects of their care.

When the stated budget is not adequate to complete the lifetime strategy for dental health and your treatment recommendations do not address all of their concerns, they will quickly realize there must be a discrepancy between what they need and what they can afford.

Always assume, unless patients tell you otherwise, that dollar figures represent an annual budget. Remember that patients still have to get used to the idea of a lifetime dental health strategy. Most still think in terms of per-visit costs. It's already a stretch for them to consider annual costs, much less a lifetime dental budget.

What do we tell Mrs. Leonard when her stated budget is well below the anticipated cost for her care? Say, "Here's what we can do for you this year. We'll repair your lower front teeth and completely rebuild your upper front teeth with porcelain crowns, just as we talked about earlier. Next year we can address the missing back teeth, when this care might fit better into your budget."

You know what her response will be. "You mean I can't get all my teeth fixed?!"

Tell her calmly, "Mrs. Leonard, I'm very careful to recommend only the treatment my patients say they can afford. The care I recommended for you is a great start for your lifetime strategy. Next year we can do more and, depending on your budget, we can complete your care."

This response is what no-contest dentistry is all about. You're not selling anything; you're not arguing. Rather, you're encouraging patients to stay within their budget. You're offering the patient value.

Look at all you've accomplished. First, your patient knows you know her case by heart. That in itself can sell a lot of dentistry. Patients realize you've planned and sequenced their care based on their reality, not yours. You haven't once fallen into the "You have a problem. I'll sell you the solution." trap. Because of your nonconfrontational, no-contest approach, patients like and trust you enough to have returned for three appointments. They have experienced value at each appointment. They sense you offer a safe, nonjudgmental place to get their teeth fixed. You've established enormous credibility with patients by taking time to discuss budget concerns, and you haven't embarrassed them by offering more care than they can afford. There are no winners or losers in no-contest dentistry, just satisfied participants.

OFFER NO OPTIONS

The no-contest approach does not offer multiple treatment plans, each with its own fee. Giving patients various options for performing complex dentistry only makes things more complicated and reinforces the barriers in patients' minds. Instead of telling patients, "You have a problem, I'll sell you the solution," the multiple treatment plan approach says, "You have a problem, so you pick a solution and I'll sell it to you." Neither message is the one you want your patients to receive.

The no-contest case presentation is not an exercise in showing patients how many different ways there are to treat them. Instead, it offers one treatment plan that can be implemented over time. If patients' budgets don't meet the costs for the total package of care, you can use the stated figures to get them started on a program of lifetime dental health care. Complex restorative dentistry can often be delivered in phases over a period of years.

Of course, there are patients where segmented treatment plans will not work because of technical considerations. In those instances, recommend temporization and the use of all plastic partial dentures to restore planes of occlusion and other strategies that will help patients get into a holding pattern. Use common sense and apply their budgets to accomplish the foundational work that ultimately will lead them to their lifetime strategy.

There are as many reasons, however, for not determining patients' budgets before making treatment recommendations as there are skeptical dentists. Some ask, "Won't patients be offended if they suspect I'm planning treatment based on the size of their wallet?" Others declare, "I'm a quality dentist. When my patients realize that, my fees won't stop them." Or, "I offer the best treatment I know how and if patients can't afford it, that's not my problem."

Imagine what a difference it would make if you knew before you finalized treatment plans what your patient's budget was. Even the most skeptical dentists admit knowing a patient's budget beforehand makes the planning and communication process much better for everyone. That's the purpose of no-contest dentistry.

PATIENT FINANCIAL ARRANGEMENTS
AND PAYMENT OPTIONS

The financial arrangements with our patients have been kept as simple as possible. For the first several years of my practice we required one-half of the total treatment fee when care started and the balance before the final prosthesis was inserted. Eventually, our financial arrangements evolved to one-third of the total treatment fee when we started, one-third due at the middle of care, and the balance due before the final prosthesis was inserted. We liked the latter arrangements better because the one-third down payment allowed patients to start easier and we received the majority of our fee before we were finished.

Dental insurance was filed for the patient when treatment was complete and assignment of benefits went to the patient. All financial arrangements were strictly between the patient and us. We discouraged patients filing pretreatment estimates because we found they delayed and discouraged care. We explained that pretreatment estimates were really pretreatment denials. If the patient insisted we file a pretreatment estimate, we charged a $25 administrative fee payable before the filing. Understand that pretreatment estimates (denials) for reconstructive care are complex and time consuming.

When pretreatment estimates were completed and reviewed by the insurance company, they never resulted in establishing a better doctor/patient relationship. The statements of the insurance companies—that our fees were above the usual and customary fees—always started a contest with the patient. We took a hard line on keeping the insurance company out of the doctor/patient relationship. Did I loose patients over this inflexible policy? Of course. But I never lost sleep fuming over the insurance company's antics of obstruction of care. And our practice thrived despite our hard-line policy.

During over 20 years of full-time practice, we rarely sent out statements and enjoyed more than 100 percent collections consistently. We had a strictly cash basis. We never offered time payment plans where we were financing the care. Time payment plans for reconstructive care are time bombs! We avoided the snares of patient financing. Some patients who owe you money and are falling on financial hard times will find reasons not to pay you. They will begin to find fault with your dentistry and leverage those faults into reasons not to pay you. Patients who owe you money and are not making their payments will not refer to you and will not keep their recall appointments. This behavior only compounds any clinical problems that are likely to occur over time. The complex reconstruction has a 100 percent probability that some area in time will need retreatment. When the patient owes you money and is experiencing real clinical problems, you can expect a colossal contest over who will pay for the recare.

And, of course, the patient holds the ultimate trump card when engaged in the contest of who will pay for the treatment: the malpractice lawsuit. Often the easiest solution to resolve their previous financial commitment to you is to sue you. They will not have any trouble finding attorneys and expert witnesses to side with them. Time payment plans offered by the practice are a predictable path to contests about money and lawsuits. You cannot win in either circumstance.

We attempted many times to find suitable third party financing for our patients. I made financing option arrangements with our local bank. I had brochures explaining the types of finance plans and the tax consequences of each. Most people who were considering financing their care rarely used our sources of credit, preferring to use their own. Retrospectively, I'm glad they did. My experience with patient financing taught me the more I removed myself from between the financing institution and the patient, the easier my life was.

We offered a dental credit card, other health care credit cards, MasterCharge, and Visa. Usually the charges placed on credit cards were less than $5,000 and did not create major contests. Credit card financing was the least invasive to the doctor/patient relationship.

Early in my career I was eager to find ways to help patients pay for our care. Over time I learned it was not good business to encourage patients to incur debt. Those who did not have the financial strength to pay for their care and used debt instruments were a greater clinical and medical/legal liability than were patients who could afford care without going into debt. I preferred to treat reconstruction patients in segments that were affordable out of their cash flow, thus stretching the total treatment plan out over time. The realization that debt contributed to clinical and medical/legal problems was one of the prime factors that lead to the creation of our budget-based No-contest case presentation.

THINK OF IT AS REAL ESTATE

The principles used in the no-contest case review for reconstructive dentistry are more closely linked to the retail/service sector of business than they are to health care delivery.

Traditional health care is primarily hospital-based, non-elective, and insurance financed. Reconstructive dentistry, on the other hand, is elective, performed on an outpatient basis, and paid for by the patient. Strictly from a consumer's point of view, it makes sense to structure the reconstructive dentistry process from a retail point of view.

Operating from a retail perspective simply means offering outstanding value and service geared to the specific customer's budget. It's done routinely in the real estate industry. The process a typical agent goes through with home buyers has definite parallels to no-contest dentistry.

My wife, Carolyn, is a real estate sales associate. She often gets calls from young couples interested in buying a home. After collecting some initial information, she arranges to meet this couple in her office. Here the potential buyers discuss their interests, so Carolyn can get a good idea about the type of home they want. But they can't go much further until they also discuss what they can afford. Even in this first meeting, it's appropriate to discuss budget.

To help determine what price range of home the couple can afford, Carolyn considers their budget—take-home pay, other sources of income, car payments, credit card payments, alimony, and other monthly debts. Consequently, within 10 or 20 minutes of their first meeting with Carolyn, the buyers are divulging all of their private financial information. Are they offended? Are they shocked? Of course not. Most people consider it a valuable service to have a realtor help them make financial decisions regarding the purchase of a home. These buyers are not offended because they *expect* to have such conversations with their real estate agent. It's this expectation that clears the path to acceptance.

What do dental patients expect? Right now they expect to be treated like they always have been—you have a problem. I'll sell you a solution—who knows if you can afford it or not? What dentists need to do is create a different kind of expectation in their patients, one that emphasizes the importance of determining a dental budget before treatment decisions are made and indicates clearly that it's okay to talk about what things cost.

To create the proper expectations for the case review appointment, start at the diagnostic appointment phase. Let your message be clear: "Next time, we're talking about money. Prepare yourself. Get ready. Expect it. It's okay." When patients know going in that you're going to ask them about their budget, it clears the path to acceptance.

As much as we might like to think otherwise, all treatment plans are budget-driven. There are very few people willing to accept rehabilitative dentistry without considering its costs, even when their budgets will more than cover the expense. It's essential to position the concept of budget as another diagnostic variable to be considered during treatment planning. Knowing patients' budgets is as fundamental to the successful implementation of no-contest dentistry as knowing their medical history. Fees rank at the top of the list of deterrents to dental care. By opening the door early to budget considerations, you're offering patients an outstanding value. Once financial discussions begin, patients see more possibilities than they had previously imagined.

In the industry of real estate, agents qualify their clients by their ability to afford homes in a particular price range. Then they show them only those homes they can afford. If realtors conducted their business like dentists, however, here's what would happen: As soon as prospective buyers entered the office we'd herd them into our gold Lincoln Town Car, we'd drive them to the richest neighborhoods in town. "Now this is what I would buy if I were buying a home," we'd say.

We'd show them the houses we'd most like to sell and explain the quality construction in minute detail. "Look at that Sheetrock. It's the best money can buy. Look at this lawn—nothing but premium quality sod." Then we'd go back to the office and show our clients pictures of the homes they just looked at.

When they would ask how much a certain home costs, we'd get anxious or irritated. We'd tell them, "I don't discuss costs with customers—my secretary does that."

When our prospective buyers finally left the office—never to be seen again—we'd wonder, "What was wrong with them? They must have a low house I.Q." And we'd look in the mirror and say to ourselves, "I need to take more courses on home construction."

To be successful in reconstructive dentistry, you have to qualify your buyers, and ignore traditional myths.

DANGER AHEAD

Pitfalls are plentiful for dentists who present high-fee procedures without first qualifying their buyer/patients. A great way to make patients angry is to quote high fees without knowing what they can afford. Consider the following scenario:

Your patient, a retired schoolteacher, is anxiously waiting with her husband to hear your treatment plan. You feel good about your relationship with this woman. She's full of compliments about everything you do, and even brought a homemade German chocolate cake for the staff the last time she was in.

Her husband smiles and is pleased to see her so happy and filled with expectation. Finally, his wife is going to get her teeth fixed—something she's wanted all her life. He is really proud of himself because he is helping her do it. In many ways, this is a dream come true.

There's just one problem. You've failed to discuss their budget.

Your case presentation is technical wonder. After each detailed description of the treatment you propose, you produce picture after picture of the wonderful work you've done in the past. Both the woman and her husband are leaning forward, smiling in anticipation. Then it happens.

He asks, "Tell me, Doc, how much is all this going to cost?"

You reply with confidence, "The fee for everything I've discussed here is $13,500."

Their bubble of enthusiasm bursts with an almost audible "pop." This is a very devaluing experience.

Your patient forces a small, quivering smile in your direction. Then she glances nervously at her husband who sits motionless, his expression set in stone. She knows what that expression means; it means they cannot afford it.

The husband's first emotion is embarrassment. He's lived too long not to be able to afford this really wonderful thing for his wife. Slowly, his embarrassment turns to anger, directed first at himself—then at you.

His wife tries desperately to bridge the gap between you and him with her eyes. Then she begins to sink as her husband declares, "You know, Doc, if we had any idea it was going to be that expensive, we wouldn't have wasted your time."

You try to recover by offering alternatives, but by now no one is listening. Your tone of voice and body language show your frustration and impatience. Your patient is disappointed, her husband embarrassed and angry. You've played the game, and everyone has lost. It's a completely devaluing experience for everyone.

Every time this scenario is repeated, it builds mental barriers in your mind that keep you from offering complete dentistry. Each time patients repeat such an experience, the walls that keep them from accepting complete dentistry rise higher.

There is a simple remedy to keep these barriers from forming: Know the budget before you offer treatment.

Will every patient tell you a specific annual dollar amount they can afford? No, they won't. Some may say, "I have no idea what to expect. You tell me, you're the doctor." Others may say, "Give me an idea of what my choices are and what each costs, and we'll go from there."

These are legitimate responses that occur often. When they do occur, you really have no choice but to quote the fee for the entire lifetime strategy for dental health. If they balk at the fee, remind them that this work can be done in increments over time. Ask them again what best fits into their budget; tell them you'll engineer the plan to fit their budget and priorities. Patients who are really stubborn about agreeing on a budget eventually understand what you are trying to do for them.

Keep in mind an important principle. Recommend only that portion of care that is within the budget. Dental care beyond the budget is targeted for succeeding years. With this approach the chances are excellent the patient will ask you . . .

THE BEST QUESTION IN DENTISTRY

"Well, Doc, I understand you're recommending only the treatment that's within my budget, but what would it cost if we went ahead and did the whole thing?" This is the best question in dentistry. It represents overwhelming approval of the no-contest case presentation process. Patients are now giving you permission to quote a fee for the entire lifetime strategy for dental health.

When patients who need $12,000 worth of dentistry but have the budget for only $5,000 ask this question, you know you've succeeded in conveying the no-contest message. You have protected them from embarrassment by recommending only that treatment that fits within their budget. Any procedures that go beyond their stated budget will come as their own recommendations, not yours. When the patient asks you the best question in dentistry, it indicates you have communicated that value is available in your office, and they want more of it. There's no better position for you than this.

Approaching rehabilitative case presentations on a no-contest basis gives you many opportunities to offer incremental treatments within the context of a complete lifetime strategy for dental health.

THE VALUE OF PATIENT EDUCATION

During the time I was rebuilding my new patient procedures toward the no-contest approach, I experimented with various techniques to lead patients into wanting comprehensive care. I wanted patients to ask me for reconstructive care, so that my staff and I could focus on providing care instead of making sales.

One of the techniques I used was providing patient education and home-care introduction in conjunction with a hygiene appointment. I wanted to use the hygiene/home care/patient education aspect more in my practice to offer and highlight value *prior to* my recommendations for care. The goal was to bring patients to a heightened state of awareness (dental I.Q.) and to create an appetite for reconstructive care, as well as to give them proper training to prevent future dental disease.

I investigated patient education techniques other successful offices used, read volumes on soft tissue management programs, and attended seminars. I also bought most of the home-care aids designed for educating patients and raising their level of appreciation for excellent dental health (i.e. electric toothbrushes, floss aids, special toothbrushes, special mouthwashes, irrigation devices, video programs, pamphlets, and intraoral cameras). For patients with more advanced periodontal conditions, I would appoint multiple hygiene appointments for root planning and home-care instruction and evaluation.

Initially, I thought the approach was well accepted. I knew the traditional, textbook approach to reconstructive dentistry dictated that periodontal and patient education factors be implemented prior to the reconstructive diagnostic phase. In a perfect world, all patients would have optimal periodontal health, be experts at home-care procedures, and be highly motivated to maintain those procedures for a lifetime—all *prior to* any restorative work being done for them. Some clinicians I studied with advocated not planning treatments for patients until they demonstrated for a six-month period that they had the knowledge and the willingness to maintain a plaque-free mouth.

I experienced a mixed response to the hygiene/home-care patient education approach to building value within my practice. Keep in mind my practice was exclusively advanced reconstructive dentistry. Most of my patients had advanced dental breakdown of the teeth, supporting structures, and existing dentistry. Most patients were disappointed by the condition of their mouths and ready to give up and move to dentures. Many of them already had dentures.

My hygiene/home-care patient education approach to building value was generally well accepted by my patients with relatively healthy mouths. These patients would experience one hygiene appointment, with one follow-up appointment. Home care would be reinforced and patients would receive a hygiene aid such as an irrigation device or electric toothbrush (Roto Dent). Patients without major dental breakdown commented favorably on our hygiene/home-care/patient education approach to building value.

Patients with major dental breakdown, however, didn't find this approach valuable. In fact, many of them found it to be a devaluing experience. The most consistent objection reconstructive patients had was they were eager to begin reconstructive care, and the multiple root-planing appointments were not addressing the benefits they were seeking. This objection is the classic one restorative dentists hear from their patients regarding referrals to periodontists. Patients were discouraged by the discomfort and appearance of their teeth, and multiple root planing made their mouths more uncomfortable and not a bit more aesthetic. Local anesthetic was often needed to reach some areas. I've yet to treat a patient who enjoys the needle. Additionally, the time and expense of the multiple hygiene education appointments were using resources (time and money) they would prefer to use on reconstructive care.

More objections to the hygiene/home-care/patient education approach to building value centered around providing redundant information. Many patients said they already knew how to take care of themselves. Many of them had already been through this approach. It was their discomfort, disillusionment, and disappointment that sapped their eagerness and willingness to perform scrupulous hygiene procedures—not their lack of knowledge. Many of them objected to multiple appointments on home-care and root planing and interpreted our home-care instructions as preachy and judgmental.

Over time, I realized the traditional textbook perfect-world approach to home care, hygiene, and periodontal issues needed to be altered. It needed to be altered to harmonize with patients' perceptions of value and comply with standards of care regarding periodontal and prevention issues.

I gradually evolved my approach to the patient education and hygiene component of care. In its "final" form, this component of care was implemented after treatment was accepted and temporary restorations were in place. Here is an example of how I might reposition patient education and hygiene for a typical partially edentulous full-mouth reconstructive patient, assuming this patient had acceptable medical history.

I would complete all diagnostic, case presentation, and consent procedures allowing for contingencies of additional tooth loss, poor healing, and referrals. At the first restorative appointment, I would have on hand processed temporary restorations and full capability for periodontal and tooth-removal surgery. I would prepare the sextant of teeth with either full crowns or bridgework, or remove existing dentistry and prepare the sextant to support temporary restorations that were in harmony with the final planes of occlusion and vertical dimension. Just before cementation of the temporary restorations, I would use an ultrasonic scaler to root plane the teeth in the sextant I was working. With the teeth prepared, contacts opened, and occlusal heights reduced, it would be quicker and easier to do a more thorough job of reaching all the root surfaces. Anesthetic was already in the area. Often my hygienist could hand scale a sextant or an entire arch in a fraction of the time with superior results.

Tooth extractions would be completed and temporary restorations cemented. Eventually, all sextants would receive the same treatment: tooth preparations, removal of existing dentistry, root planing, tooth extractions, and temporization. Endodontic procedures, bite adjustments, and phonetic adjustments would follow.

Within one month of the first restorative appointment, my patients would have temporary restorations with near complete comfort of bite, soft tissues, appearance, and speech. At this point in their care, I would initiate the hygiene/home-care/patient education component. Patients now had a reason to listen. The instruction we were giving them was within the context of their new dentistry, not their failing dentistry. After all, what are you more interested in—washing your new car or your old one?

All the hygiene aids were demonstrated on their new mouth, not their old mouth. Soft tissues were much more comfortable and home care was easier, hence we saw more compliance.

If the patient required more advanced periodontal care, implants, or preprosthetic surgical procedures, this care was completed with local anesthetics at subsequent appointments. Home care was reinforced at suture-removing appointments in the context of helping patients understand that plaque-free environments heal better. Now home care was not perceived as preaching. Its value lay in its therapeutic affect on healing, and everyone wants to heal faster and better.

After the periodontal structures were within normal limits, final tooth preparations would be made, temporaries relined, and, ultimately, final restorations placed.

Our hygiene/home-care/patient education component blended in with our ongoing restorative and surgical procedures. We eliminated the resistance of preoperative hygiene and home-care appointments by repositioning them in the sequence of care. More importantly, we anchored the importance of home care in the minds of patients by demonstrating its value within the context of their new dentistry.

It has been my observation that patients respond positively to the repositioned hygiene and patient education appointments. I began to see the traditional textbook approach to hygiene and patient education in a context of the real-world reconstructive patient. In my previous approach, well-meaning acts of the initial hygiene appointment and suggestions regarding home-care techniques were often misinterpreted by patients as judgmental and scolding. Patients were impatient with the process and almost all experienced discomfort and costs (time and money) with no corresponding apparent value.

Therapeutically, I was able to produce a superior clinical result initiating root planing at mid-treatment.

Home-care instructions and compliance were much greater when given in the context of enhancing the healing process and preserving their new dentistry.

In a perfect world, the traditional approach to the hygiene and patient education appointments make sense when positioned at the beginning of the treatment plan. Patients should recognize its value, be thankful for the clinician's approach, and proceed with reconstructive procedures. However, my experience in the real world of reconstructive dentistry is that the traditional approach did not offer value from the patient's point of view. In many cases, it devalued the treatment experience. Patients became impatient, discouraged, and discontinued treatment. By repositioning the hygiene and patient education appointments mid-treatment, I was able to demonstrate its value with greater impact and provide a superior clinical result. I came to think of patient education like swimming upstream—it's easier when you go with the flow.

Remember, we are not altering the final result of the treatment plan. We are altering the time it takes to keep the treatment plan within the annual budget. You'll find that many $10,000 treatment plans get done in $5,000 increments. And doesn't it make more sense to treat two patients for $5,000 each than none for $10,000?

Do all patients accept lifetime strategies for dental health? Of course not. Many patients learn that their budgets are no where near what it takes to rehabilitate their mouths. But you have not embarrassed them or made them angry. They can remain patients in your practice and alternative, less expensive treatment plans within their budget can be developed.

Here's a sample dialogue of the records review appointment. Our patient Wanda Leonard has brought her husband with her today. They are both seated in the consult area. I review her record, memorizing the overall treatment sequence and fees. Wanda's treatment plan includes reconstruction of all her remaining teeth and two implant-supported bridges in her posterior mandible. Her total treatment fee is $18,000. My receptionist tells me her husband's name is Jack.

Dr. Homoly: Hello, Mrs. Leonard. Good to see you. And you must be Jack Leonard. I'm Paul Homoly. Welcome to our office.

Mrs. Leonard: I brought Jack with me today because we had some questions about my care.

Dr. Homoly: That's fine. Can I answer any of those questions now?

Mrs. Leonard: I guess the biggest question is what exactly are you going to do for me?

Dr. Homoly: Let me show what we can do for you, depending on what's appropriate for your budget and schedule. Your biggest problem is the loose lower partial denture. And our X-rays and examination show that the lower front teeth need rebuilding.

Mrs. Leonard: Yes, they do. I've noticed they're all worn down and have chipped edges.

Dr. Homoly: Your upper front and back teeth also show advanced wear. At some point in your lifetime strategy, all your upper teeth will need rebuilding. Your budget will help us decide when to do that.

Mrs. Leonard: What about my missing lower back teeth? How would you fix them?

Dr. Homoly: Dental implants will give us the best bite and make chewing the most comfortable. When we do that will depend on your budget. Last time we talked a little about your budget. Before I make any concrete recommendations for you, I need to know what's appropriate for your budget, and I know you want to take full advantage of your insurance. Do you have an annual budget we need to stay within?

Jack quickly speaks up. They need to maximize their insurance. He's done his homework and realizes their policy will allow $1,200 a year. Wanda's previous dentist has already told them that their fee could range from $3,000 to $8,250. Jack's concern is how much above their insurance Wanda's care will be and how they'll have to pay for it.

Dr. Homoly: Is there an annual amount over what the insurance will pay that we need to stay within?

Mrs. Leonard: There is, Dr. Homoly. We really can't spend any more than $5,000 on my dentistry. Can you do it for that?

Dr. Homoly: Yes we can. We can get an excellent start on your lifetime strategy and stay within your budget. Let me show you what I recommend.

At this point, I describe full mouth equilibration, three quadrants of root planning, four mandibular anterior all-porcelain crowns, ceramo metal crowns on #22 and #27 with distal ERA attachments, and an all-plastic removable partial denture with ERA attachments.

Dr. Homoly: The total fee for this care is $4,990 and will take me about two months to complete.

Mrs. Leonard: That sounds fine, but what about my upper teeth that you said would need rebuilding? And didn't you say that implants would give me the best result?

Dr. Homoly: I did. I'm very careful to recommend only the treatment my patients say they can afford. The care I recommended for you is a great start for your lifetime strategy. Next year we can do more and, depending on your budget, we can complete your care.

Mrs. Leonard: I'll have to wait until next year before I can get the rest of my teeth fixed? I was hoping we could do it all at once. What would it cost if we went ahead and did the whole thing?

Dr. Homoly: The total fee is $18,000 and would take us about a year to complete.

Mrs. Leonard: Whoa! That's way over our budget. I had no idea how much this would cost. I don't think we can spend that much. Jack shifts his weight in the chair and crosses his arms.

Dr. Homoly: That's why I'm recommending we do only the portion that's within this year's budget. I'm doing the most important work first. Over the next few years we can go at your pace, and one day, you'll be completed.

Mrs. Leonard: When we're done with this year's work, what would you do next?

Dr. Homoly: I'd rebuild the upper front teeth next. When you're ready for the implants on the lower, I'll build the upper and lower back teeth together. If $5,000 a year is a good budget for you, we can have you done in three and a half years.

Mrs. Leonard: Is what you're planning to do this year going to make my bite comfortable? I can't wait three and a half years to get some relief.

Dr. Homoly: It will, Wanda. When would you like to start?

Here's another dialogue with Mr. Crawford, the auto mechanic, during the records review appointment. Mr. Crawford is seated in the consult area. I review his record, memorizing the overall treatment sequence and fees. Mr. Crawford's treatment plan includes two four-unit bridges replacing missing mandibular posterior teeth. Additionally, he needs five single-unit crowns with build-ups in his posterior maxilla and aggressive root planning and equilibration. His total treatment fee is $11,500. My receptionist tells me he's in a hurry.

Dr. Homoly: Hello, Mr. Crawford. Good to see you. I understand you're in a hurry today. If you need to leave now we can reschedule this.

Mr. Crawford: No, let's get to this. I'm doing all my chewing on my front teeth. How are you gonna fix my mouth, Doc?

Dr. Homoly: What we do for you depends on what's appropriate for your budget and schedule. Your biggest problem is the loose lower partial denture. And our X-rays and examination show that some of the upper back teeth need rebuilding. Last time I asked if you had a budget we needed to stay within. Did you give that any more thought?

Mr. Crawford: I don't know, Doc. Tell me what I need and what my options are, and we'll go from there.

Dr. Homoly: Your missing lower back teeth can be replaced with nonremovable teeth. Some of your upper back teeth will need rebuilding. Your budget will help us decide when and how much we do at one time. What's most important to you?

Mr. Crawford: I need to eat, Doc. Let's fix the lower first. How much is that gonna cost?

Dr. Homoly: About $6,000. It will take us four to five appointments. Is that within your budget?

Mr. Crawford: Six thousand bucks! That's a lot of money, Doc. I don't know if I can handle that. What else can you do?

Dr. Homoly: What I can do is phase your treatment over time to stay within a budget you can handle. If you can budget $3,000 a year for your teeth, I can have you in first-class shape within three to four years.

Mr. Crawford: You mean it's gonna take $12,000 to fix my mouth? You can buy a new car for that, Doc.

Dr. Homoly: We can get an excellent start on your lifetime strategy and stay within a $3,000 annual budget. Let me show you what I'd do.

At this point, I describe minor equilibration, three quadrants of root planning, and one posterior four-unit bridge.

Dr. Homoly: The total fee for this care is $3,750 and will take me about two months to complete. Next year we can do more and, depending on your budget, we can complete your care.

Mr.Crawford: What would you do next?

Dr. Homoly: I'd replace the missing teeth on the other side of your lower jaw. I'll rebuild the upper back teeth all at once. If $3,000 a year is a good budget for you, we can have you done in four years.

Mr. Crawford: Will I be able to chew with just one side fixed? I won't wait four years to be able to eat.

Dr. Homoly: You'll chew much better than you do now, but not as good as when we're all done. When would you like to start?

You'll know your approach has worked when you and your patient are not uptight about money. Budget-based treatment planning gets all the cards on the table for

you and the patient. It defuses the anxiety normally related to discussing fees.

CHANGE YOURSELF

What if a patient needs $5,000 worth of dentistry but
has planned a vacation or wants to buy a car? How do
you get that patient to change priorities and put dental
care in front of other purchases? The answer is, you can't.
You must change your priorities.

It's a common myth in the dental industry that the quality of our work will lead patients to desire dental care
above other priorities. If you continue to think you can
change patients' behavior, you'll be disappointed. Occasionally, patients can be scared into treatment, but most
will do what they want, when they want, regardless of
what you say or do. Instead of getting frustrated at attempts to change patients' priorities, change yourself.
Determine in your mind that no matter what decisions
your patients make, you'll interpret them as something
positive. You can't control other people's decisions, but
you can choose your own responses. Learning to control your responses is an important step in mastering
the no-contest technique. It's a skill that will accelerate
your personal and professional growth.

There's a learning process related to being able to choose
our responses. The first step is realizing you can. The
anger, worry, frustration, and disappointment that seem
so common in the dental office are choices we make.
These choices are not the only options we have. Once
we become aware that there are other options, we have

completed the first major step in the direction of choosing how we will react to events.

A good way to learn to control your responses is to have a picture in your mind of the kind of professional you want to become. Try to identify specific character qualities you'd like to develop. When situations arise, ask yourself, "How would the dentist I want to become respond?" The dentist you hope to become would most certainly choose responses that support positive growth and mental well-being.

The ability to make conscious responses spills over naturally into all areas of personal growth. When confronted with difficult situations in private life, ask yourself, "How would the spouse (parent, friend, etc.) I want to become respond?" The healthy responses you learn to use in the practice of dentistry become the responses you demonstrate in everyday life. What works in the dental office works at home.

You can avoid much of the stress associated with dentistry today by recognizing that you can control your responses. Expecting patients to change their priorities for your convenience only sets the stage for a career filled with disappointment and stress. Instead, focus on changing your own reactions and choosing a healthy response. When you're at your best, you'll perform at your best for those patients who have made good dental health a high priority.

The Case Discussion Letter

The Write Offspring

Our next chapter details the value of the case discussion letter as a positioning tool for the practice. The case discussion letter is described in detail as are ideas for its implementation. Here are the highlights of this chapter.

- The anatomy and physiology of the case discussion letter
- Reproducing case discussion letters
- More ways to differentiate yourself and create solid reasons for patients to accept fee-for-service dentistry.

If you want to be positioned as unique in the minds of your patients, you must provide value beyond their expectations. The case discussion letter is a personal communication from you and creates a powerful environment for fee-for-service care to prosper.

THE CASE DISCUSSION LETTER
When was the last time you received a letter from your physician summarizing the results of your latest physical exam and offering health recommendations?

Probably never. When was the last time patients received a letter from you outlining the findings of their examination and offering dental health recommendations? Again, probably never. How many of your next new patients have received a letter from their previous dentists explaining a lifetime strategy for dental health. Very few, if any.

If you want to be positioned as unique and special in the minds of your patients, you must provide value beyond their expectations. A powerful way to do this is to communicate with them in writing. The case discussion letter is a personal communication from you to an individual patient. It's a valuable positioning tool that differentiates your practice from all others. It is unique and powerfully effective.

Send the case discussion letter after you have discussed the recommended treatment within the patient's stated budget. There's nothing difficult about producing this letter. You simply summarize the results of an individual's dental exam and review the budgeted treatment recommendations you have previously discussed. Its value lies not in producing it, but in its message to patients that you took extra time especially for them. Very few, if any, other dentists have done this before.

To be most effective, a case discussion letter should be mailed within one week following the case discussion appointment. Send it unfolded in a large, hand-addressed envelope. Have your letter proofread carefully for any errors in grammar usage, spelling, and punctuation. You may also want to include brochures about specific specialty procedures (implants, cosmetic dentistry, etc.) the patient will receive, along with your business card and office brochure.

Following is an example of how such a letter can be structured, complete with the management objectives of each section. This letter goes to Mrs. Leonard, a candidate for complex reconstructive dentistry.

Initial Greeting—Tell Mrs. Leonard how pleased you are to have her as a patient. Be sure to include the date of her last visit and any pertinent personal information you may recall. Perhaps she just returned from a European vacation or sent fudge to the office staff. A warm, friendly greeting assures patients you really do know who they are, that their concerns are important to you, and that you intend to take very good care of them.

Chief Dental Concern—Reiterate the chief dental concern that brought Mrs. Leonard to you in the first place. Take the information directly from the dental history portion of her record and your initial interview notes. The objective in repeating this information is to demonstrate that you have heard and understood her concerns.

Therapeutic Approach—Restate and define the concept of the lifetime strategy for dental health. It's not enough to introduce the concept in your office once and expect patients to grasp it fully. The lifetime dental health strategy should be the identifying feature of your approach to dentistry; it's what makes you unique. Mention it often.

Summary of Examination—Briefly outline the findings of Mrs. Leonard's latest exam. It is not necessary to provide every detail. Hit the high points and write in plain English. If you have to use technical terms, be sure to clearly define them.

Medical and Dental History—Relate the patient's medical health to her dental health. Here you have an excellent opportunity to educate patients by showing how dental problems can affect overall health. You might point out, for example, that poor dental health may be responsible for digestive problems.

Soft Tissue and Oral Cancer Screening Evaluation—Include the findings of these studies to heighten her awareness of the thoroughness of your examination. If your patient uses tobacco in any form, this section of the letter should outline the hazards of tobacco use and its relation to dental disease. Don't preach, just state the facts. The ADA has excellent pamphlets on smoking and its effect on oral health.

Treatment Objectives and Recommendations—Give a general overview of the recommended treatment that falls within Mrs. Leonard's budget while avoiding any mention of fees. Use straightforward language and brief descriptions. Too much detail may confuse patients and create the opportunity for your letter to become a shopping list for second opinions. Keep it simple.

Prognosis—Offer your opinion about the expected outcome based on the treatment recommendations. Be enthusiastic yet realistic in your expectations. Don't promise what you can't guarantee or deliver. A conservative estimate of what patients can expect assures them they have made a good decision in selecting you as their dentist, and that you have the skills necessary to do the work they need done.

Benefits of Care—Remind your patient why this dental treatment is being done and reinforce once again that it addresses her chief dental concern.

Next Appointment Reminder—By confirming the time and activity planned for the next appointment, you encourage patients to continue with their care plan. The message implied in the reminder is that you have set aside time exclusively for this individual because you take her care seriously.

P.S.—Use the postscript to remind Mrs. Leonard of any critical issues related to the business aspects of her dental care. Direct mail studies have shown that the postscript portion of a letter is consistently noticed and read. Make sure you leave on a positive note.

The most difficult aspect of implementing the case discussion letter as part of your practice procedure is getting started. But after the first 10 letters or so, you will notice many similarities in content. With a good word processing program, you should be able to customize a personal letter from a standard format in about 20 minutes. Use spelling and grammar checking programs to check your letter before it's printed.

The case discussion letter is not a guarantee that patients will follow through with treatment. Things come up that delay care. It's been my personal experience that patients do not discard this letter even though they may postpone care.

Keep in mind the cumulative effect it will have in your practice. For example, if you see 20 new patients per month and half of them accept the concept of the lifetime strategy for dental health, you'll be sending out 10 follow-up letters a month. At the end of a year you'll have 120 letters; at the end of two years you'll have close to 250. The case discussion letters are the offspring of your family of patients.

What effect will over 200 case discussion letters have on your practice? Again, my personal experience has been that it has enormous impact on retaining patients who have postponed treatment.

The case discussion letter is a crucial vertebrae in the backbone of the no-contest case presentation process. The sooner you start the better.

January 20, 1992

Pat Seminar
10821 Waxhaw Road
Charlotte, NC 28277

Dear Pat,

I thought you would appreciate a summary of the conversation we had on January 16 about my findings and recommendations for treatment.

Chief Dental Concern—

During our initial interview and subsequent conversations, you expressed dissatisfaction with the appearance and chewing ability of your teeth as well as sensitivity in your front teeth.

Therapeutic Approach—

A therapeutic approach relates to the level of dental care you request. You have indicated to me that you are interested in an approach that incorporates a lifetime strategy for dental health. A lifetime strategy includes:

1. Keeping infection from destroying teeth, gums, and bone. In your case, we want to prevent more bone loss from occurring around your teeth and jaws.

2. Replacing and restoring missing teeth in a way that will enhance comfort, function, and appearance.

3. Monitoring your dental health periodically.

4. Retreating areas that may require revisions due to changes in your overall health, accidents, infection, loss of bone, or breakage of materials.

A lifetime strategy for dental care blends the art and science of dentistry with the everyday realities of your lifestyle, personal attitudes about health, and your budget. With the technology that exists in dentistry today, almost anyone, regardless of current dental disease, can be brought to a level of excellence in dental comfort, function, and appearance.

You have asked me to evaluate your care within the perspective of a lifetime strategy, Pat. My first responsibility is to perform a complete examination and communicate to you the current state of your dental health. My next responsibility is to help you develop a strategy for dental health care consistent with your lifestyle, attitudes about health, and individual budget.

Summary of Examination

Missing Teeth. Currently, you have 10 missing teeth.

Gum and Bone Health. The health of the gum and bone around your upper teeth is generally poor. Your lower teeth have better periodontal health. You have minimal pocketing of the gums, and the shape and contour of your gums is within normal limits. The areas that are most affected by gum disease on your lower jaw are your left and right back teeth. Your lower front teeth also demonstrate gum disease. These teeth have moderate bone loss. As you know periodontal disease is a slowly progressive disease. The gum therapy Dr. Dontist performed for you has done well. It has enabled you to keep some very compromised teeth up to this point. Dr. Dontist and I will monitor the health of your gums and make revisions as necessary.

Bite Analysis. Your occlusion (the relationship and position of your upper teeth and jaw to your lower teeth and jaw) is good. Even though some of your teeth have been replaced with bridgework, the jaw relationships in your mouth are within normal limits (a key ingredient for stable teeth). As I replace some of your existing bridgework and teeth, I will harmonize the bite relationships between your teeth.

The Temporomandibular Joint. Your temporomandibular joint (jaw joint) is within normal limits. It's common for jaw joint problems to exist when many teeth are missing. Many jaw joint problems start gradually, usually in the form of a clicking or popping sound in the joint. Such joint problems can lead to joint pain, chronic headaches, dizziness, ringing in the ears, and limitation of jaw opening. Currently, you have slight joint popping in your right jaw and some limitation of opening. In your case, I would expect your jaw joint to become more comfortable when your missing teeth are replaced and the bite is harmonized.

Results of Radiographs (X-rays)

Tooth decay. There is no X-ray evidence of tooth decay, although some is present upon clinical examination.

Bone Levels. The bone level around your lower teeth and upper teeth is variable.

Root tips. There is evidence of remaining root tips (portions of teeth previously removed) in your upper right jaw.

Temporomandibular Joint. Your jaw joint appears normal in the X-ray.

Impactions. There is no evidence of impacted (unerupted) teeth.

Abscesses. I see some evidence of abscessed teeth on your X-ray. Remember, that X-ray evidence of abscess formation is not conclusive. Teeth can also be abscessed without X-ray evidence. We will have to proceed on a tooth-by-tooth basis to your dental health.

Sinus. Your sinus cavities appear clear, enlarged, and healthy.

Root Canal Fillings. You have no teeth that have been treated by root canal therapy.

Medical and Dental History

Your medical and dental histories are within normal limits and should contribute to a successful result in dental treatment. Your blood pressure at the time of the examination was excellent, reading 120/85 with a pulse of 70 beats per minute.

It is common for many of my patients who are missing teeth to have digestive and/or nutritional disorders. Stomach ulcers, intestinal ulcers, and lower bowel discomfort can be a direct result of the inability to properly chew. Digestion begins in the mouth. Teeth grind the food and mix it with digestive enzymes found in the saliva. If this process does not happen and food is swallowed partially chewed, the stomach and intestines have much more work to do. Digestive problems are the result. I'll estimate you currently have 40 percent chewing efficiency. Your digestive problems may well be a direct result of your reduced chewing ability.

I also find that my patients who are missing many of their teeth or those that have gum disease are also smokers. I am sure you have heard enough about smoking and gum disease from your previous periodontist. If you can reduce or stop smoking, your short-term healing and overall success will be greatly enhanced.

Soft Tissue and Oral Cancer Screening Evaluation

Five percent of all cancers occur in the mouth and can usually be detected early with clinical and X-ray evaluation. At your examination appointment we performed an oral cancer screening exam. The areas of the throat, palate, cheeks, lips, ridges, tongue, floor of mouth, salivary glands, neck, and face were all within normal limits. The large bone bumps on the roof of your mouth may contribute to difficulties wearing a full denture.

Treatment Objectives and Recommendations

After a review of your X-rays and examination materials, I feel confident in recommending the following approach to your dental treatment. The objectives of our treatment are threefold:

1. Elimination of the discomfort associated with your teeth

2. Replacement of missing teeth and aesthetic and functional enhancement of the upper and lower teeth

3. Prevention of recurrence of future dental disease

Your treatment will follow this general sequence:

- Removal of loose upper teeth (eight) and immediate replacement with a temporary removable partial denture.

- Elimination of the sensitivity in lower front teeth (pulp therapy).

- Insertion of implants and bone grafts in upper jaw. Implants usually require three to six months for complete healing. You will be able to wear replacement teeth during the healing process.

- Insertion of upper bridge work (nonremovable tooth replacements) and restoration of upper teeth.

- Periodic cleanings and re-examinations to monitor the health of the gums and existing dentistry. Dr. Dontist will also participate in your long term care.

As we discussed at your last appointment, your care can be completed in steps, allowing you to achieve a high degree of dental health and stay within your budget. I estimate your initial care with me will take one year to complete. Your lower teeth will then be restored when it's appropriate for you to proceed.

Prognosis

The prognosis (expected quality of result) for your treatment is good. Three major factors contribute to this prognosis:

1. You have good medical and mental health. (You can expect even better dental health if you stop smoking.)

2. You are highly motivated, which contributes to rapid healing and appropriate home care.

3. I have abundant experience treating cases like yours.

Benefits of Care

The most immediate benefit you'll experience is increased comfort in your bite and the elimination of pain in your front teeth. You will see a dramatic improvement in the appearance of your teeth and your facial profile, and you will have far less problems associated with your gums such as bleeding and mouth odor.

Two major long-term benefits of your care are 1) preservation of the bone of the upper jaw, and 2) improvement of your nutritional status. This approach to your dental care represents a strategy that will preserve your teeth and bone for a lifetime, and ultimately will contribute to improved overall health and better quality of life.

Your Next Appointment

At your next appointment we will begin treatment on the upper jaw (removing loose teeth and inserting a partial denture) and treatment of your lower front teeth. You will be sedated for this appointment, Pat. This appointment should be easy for you and will start you on the path to improved dental health.

I look forward to our relationship and will do a great job for you.

Yours for better dental health,

Dr. Paul Homoly

P.S. I have made special arrangements through First Union National Bank to offer my patients several options for financing their dental care. Enclosed is some informational material. I have arranged these financing options for patients like you, who have extensive dental needs and must stay within their budget.

Here's an example of a case discussion letter written to a patient whose treatment will be done in phases over time. Notice also that the patient has some differences from the previous example in his chief dental concerns, the therapeutic approach, and the results of his examination.

October 15, 1992

Tony Easter
107 Bunker Ridge
Charlotte, N.C. 28277

Dear Tony,

Here is a summary of the conversation we had during your last appointment concerning my findings and recommendations for treatment.

Chief Dental Concern

During our initial interview and subsequent conversations, you expressed your concern about the appearance and health of your teeth and your desire to avoid dentures. You are concerned that your teeth may be affecting your effectiveness in business and may create embarrassment.

Therapeutic Approach

This relates to the level of dental care you request. You have indicated that you are interested in an approach to your dental care that incorporates a lifetime strategy for dental health. A lifetime strategy includes:

1. Keeping infection from destroying teeth, gums, and bone. We want to prevent the front teeth from being completely unrestorable.

2. Replacing and restoring missing teeth in a way that is harmonious with your comfort, function, and appearance.

3. Staying within your budget and implementing procedures over time.

4. Monitoring your dental health periodically and preventing the recurrence of the bite problems.

A lifetime strategy to dental care blends the art and science of dentistry with the everyday realities of your lifestyle, attitudes about health, and budget. Technology exists in dentistry to bring nearly anyone, regardless of their current dental disease, to a level of excellent dental comfort, function, and appearance.

You've asked me to evaluate your care with the perspective of a lifetime strategy, Tony. My first responsibility to you is to perform a complete examination and communicate to you your current state of dental health. Next, my responsibility is to help you develop a strategy of dental health care that will coincide with your lifestyle, attitudes about health, and your budget.

Summary of Examination

Missing Teeth. Currently you have four missing teeth.

Gum and Bone Health. Your gum and bone health around your upper and lower teeth is generally good, although minor inflammation (redness and bleeding) is present. You have minimal pocketing of the gums, and the shape and contour of your gums is within normal limits.

Bite Analysis. Your occlusion (the relationship and position of your upper teeth and jaw to your lower teeth and jaw) is outside of normal limits. As you know, the front teeth are in a traumatic relationship with one another. The back teeth are more within normal limits. The key to your dental health will be in the correct restoration of your front teeth. I am developing the correct front tooth relationship on models and will show you your final result before we do it in your mouth.

The Temporomandibular Joint. Your temporomandibular joint (jaw joint) is not within normal limits. It's common for jaw joint problems to exist when teeth move and the bite is incorrect. Many jaw joint problems start gradually, usually in the form of a clicking or popping sound in the joint. Jaw joint problems can lead to joint pain, chronic headaches, dizziness, ringing in the ears, and limitation of jaw opening. In your case, I would expect your jaw joint to become more comfortable as your teeth are replaced and the bite is harmonized.

Results of Radiographs (X-rays)

Tooth decay. There is no X-ray evidence of tooth decay, although many teeth are worn.

Bone levels. The bone level around your lower teeth and upper teeth is good.

Root tips. There is no evidence of remaining root tips (portions of teeth previously removed).

Temporomandibular Joint. Your jaw joint appears normal in the X-ray.

Impactions. There is evidence of an impacted (unerupted) tooth on the upper jaw near the front part of your mouth. At this time I have no plans for its removal.

Abscesses. I see no evidence of abscessed teeth on your X-ray. One thing to keep in mind about X-ray evidence of abscess formation is that it is not conclusive to completely rule out the existence of an abscessed tooth. Teeth can be abscessed without X-ray evidence, and we have to proceed on a tooth-by-tooth basis to insure their health.

Sinus. Your sinus cavities appear clear, enlarged, and healthy.

Root Canal Fillings. You have one tooth that has been treated by root canal therapy.

Medical and Dental History

Your medical and dental history are within normal limits and should contribute to a successful result in dental treatment. As you know, stress is a component of the cause of your front tooth wear. Combining stress with your high bite strength, it is not surprising to find teeth that are worn. It has been noted during your examination that your high stress lifestyle and the advanced wear of your teeth are related.

Soft Tissue and Oral Cancer Screening Evaluation

Five percent of all cancer occurs in the mouth and usually can be detected early with clinical and X-ray evaluation. At your examination appointment we performed an oral cancer screening exam. The areas of the throat, palate, cheeks, lips, ridges, tongue, floor of mouth, salivary glands, neck, and face were all within normal limits.

Treatment Objectives and Recommendations

After a review of your X-rays and examination materials, I feel confident in recommending the following approach to your dental treatment. The objectives of our treatment are threefold:

1. Establish the correct bite
2. Replace missing teeth
3. Prevent recurrence of future dental disease

Your treatment will progress in generally the following sequence:

- I will place temporary crowns on the upper front teeth and adjust the level of the lower front teeth. The objective of this procedure is to preview the appearance, functional harmony, and speech pattern of the new positions of the upper front teeth. Additionally, I will remove the "baby" tooth and do pulp therapy (root canal) on the peg lateral (I have changed my mind on the removal of this tooth at this time.)

- I will adjust the bite relationship of the back teeth. Following this appointment we should see some improvement of the comfort of your jaw joint.
- At this time I do not think it will be necessary to open the vertical dimension of your bite.
- Once we have proven the position of the front teeth with temporary crowns, we will then be able to structure your final restorative plan.

Your Next Appointment

At your next appointment, I will answer any questions you have, show your case on the models, and begin your temporary crowns, Tony.

I look forward to our relationship and will do a great job for you.

Yours for better dental health,

Dr. Paul Homoly

P.S. I have made special arrangements through First Union National Bank to offer my patients several options for financing their dental care. Enclosed is some informational material. I have arranged these financing options for patients like you, who have extensive dental needs and must stay within their budget.

Here's an example of a case discussion letter for a totally edentulous patient who is being treated within the team approach. Our office is providing the surgical services and the referring doctor is providing the restorative services. His daughter is a dental hygienist in another state.

January 6, 1992

Ed Dentulous
P.O. Box 35
Ridgeworn, SC 29135

Dear Ed,

I thought you would appreciate a summary of the conversation we had during your last appointment, concerning my findings and recommendations for treatment. You can mail a copy of this letter to your daughter to give her an idea of your care with us. I'd be glad to speak to her.

Chief Dental Concern
During our initial interview and subsequent conversations, you expressed dissatisfaction with your removable dentures. You indicated the removable dentures contribute to difficulties in speech, eating, and appearance.

Therapeutic Approach
This relates to the level of dental care you request. You have indicated to me that you are interested in an approach to your dental care that incorporates a lifetime strategy for dental health. A lifetime strategy includes;

1. Keeping infection from destroying teeth, gums and bone. In your case, we want to prevent more bone loss from occurring around your teeth and jaws.

2. Replacing and restoring missing teeth in a way that will enhance comfort, function, and appearance.

3. Monitoring your dental health periodically.

4. Retreating areas that may require revisions due to changes in your overall health, accidents, infection, loss of bone, or breakage of materials.

A lifetime strategy to dental care blends the art and science of dentistry with the everyday realities of your lifestyle, attitudes about health, and your budget. Technology exists in dentistry to bring nearly anyone, regardless of their current dental disease, to a level of excellent dental comfort, function, and appearance.

You have asked me to evaluate your care with the perspective of a lifetime strategy, Ed. My first responsibility is to perform a complete examination and communicate to you the current state of your dental health. Next, my responsibility is to help you develop a strategy of dental health care that will coincide with your lifestyle, attitudes about health, and your budget.

Summary of Examination
Missing Teeth. Currently, you have 32 missing teeth.

Gum and Bone Health. Your gum health is generally fair. The tone and consistency of your gums is within normal limits. The soreness you experience on your lower jaw is due to the movement and pressure of the lower denture, not an active disease state. The jaw bones are healthy although they exhibit advanced resorption (shrinkage).

Bite Analysis. Your occlusion (the relationship and position of your upper teeth and jaw to your lower teeth and jaw) is fair. Even though all of your teeth are missing, the jaw relationships in your mouth are within normal limits (a key ingredient for stable teeth). Your existing dentures have a very poor bite relation to each other. Currently, when you bite together only your front teeth touch, which contributes to instability of the lower denture.

The Temporomandibular Joint. Your temporomandibular joint (jaw joint) is within normal limits. It's common for jaw joint problems to exist when many teeth are missing. Many jaw joint problems start gradually, usually in the form of a clicking or popping sound in the joint. Such joint problems can lead to joint pain, chronic headaches, dizziness, ringing in the ears, and limitation of jaw opening. Some minor jaw joint popping is present in your left joint. In your case, I would expect your jaw joint to pop less when your missing teeth are replaced and the bite is harmonized.

Results of Radiographs (X-rays)

Bone levels. You have advanced bone loss of your lower jaw. Your upper jaw has slight bone loss. The bone loss you are experiencing is a direct result of long-term denture wear. The bone loss process (resorption) will continue unless the forces from the lower denture are eliminated.

Root tips. There is no evidence of remaining root tips (portions of teeth previously removed).

Temporomandibular joint. Your jaw joint appears normal in the X-ray.

Impactions. There is no evidence of impacted (unerupted) teeth.

Sinus. Your sinus cavities appear clear, enlarged, and healthy.

Implant Bone Quality. Sufficient bone must be present to place implants. Your lower jaw bone has sufficient height and width to place implants.

Medical and Dental History

Your medical and dental history are within normal limits and should contribute to a successful result in dental treatment. Your physician, Dr. Madden, has expressed to me you would be a good candidate for this surgery.

Soft Tissue and Oral Cancer Screening Evaluation

Five percent of all cancers occur in the mouth and can usually be detected early with clinical and X-ray evaluation. At your examination appointment we performed an oral cancer screening exam. The areas of the throat, palate, cheeks, lips, ridges, tongue, floor of mouth, salivary glands, neck, and face were all within normal limits.

Treatment Objectives and Recommendations

The objective of our relationship is to establish a lifetime strategy for you to enjoy the best possible dental health.

It's important to keep the overall goal in mind as we treat individual areas. All treatment provided for you in our office will be done in context of a lifetime strategy. Dental care provided for you today will not have to be replaced to accommodate future treatment decisions.

After a review of your X-rays and examination materials, I feel confident in recommending the following approach to your dental treatment. The objectives of our treatment are threefold:

1. Elimination of the lower denture to retard the loss of bone from the lower jaw.

2. Provide a stable base for replacement teeth. Dr. Clarke Kent will make your permanent replacement teeth supported by the implant that I place. This process will restore lost function, speech, comfort, and appearance.

3. Prevention of recurrent of future dental disease.

Your treatment will follow this general sequence:

- Placement of lower implants. This process will include two separate surgeries about six months apart. During the first surgery, implants are placed. At the second surgery, we insert the heads into the implants and make temporary replacement teeth.

- Dr. Kent will make your permanent lower denture which will be entirely supported by the implant. Dr. Kent will make a new upper denture for you. Dr. Kent and I agree that your upper jaw will do well with a conventional removable denture. Implants are not needed to hold the upper denture in a stable bite.

- Regular checkups and cleanings. This phase of treatment can be completed with Dr. Kent. I can see you on an as-needed basis.

This treatment sequence represents optimal dental care.

Prognosis
The prognosis (expected quality of result) for your treatment is good. Three major factors contribute to this prognosis:

1. Your general medical and mental health is good.

2. You are highly motivated, which contributes to rapid healing and appropriate home care.

3. I have abundant experience treating cases like yours. The limiting factor of your prognosis is the thinness of the lower jaw bone. I will do my best to build your implant so it shields the jaw from future loss of bone.

Benefits of Care

The benefits to your care are numerous. The most immediate benefit you'll experience is the improvement and comfort of your bite and chewing ability. Your facial profile will be supported as well as a dramatic improvement of the appearance of your teeth.

You will experience two major long-term benefits of care: 1) preservation of the bone of the lower jaw, and 2) improvement of your nutritional status.

Your nutritional status currently is not the best it can be. With reduced ability to chew, the process of digestion is incomplete. Unchewed food causes the stomach and the intestines to work much harder at digesting food. It is very common for my patients who have had missing teeth for many years to also have digestive problems, stomach and intestinal ulcers, nutritional deficiencies, and low-energy levels. Your dental care will significantly improve your long-term nutritional status and ultimately your overall health and quality of life. This approach to your dental care represents a strategy that will help preserve your teeth and bone for your lifetime.

Your Next Appointment

At your next appointment we will discuss any clinical questions and discuss insurance and financial arrangements. During the following appointment we will do the first surgery. This will not be a difficult appointment for you, Ed. We already have the necessary diagnostic materials and are ready to begin your care.

I look forward to our relationship and will do a great job for you.

Yours for better dental health,

Dr. Paul Homoly

P.S. I have made special arrangements through First Union National Bank to offer my patients several options for financing their dental care. Enclosed is some informational material. I have arranged these financing options for patients like you, who have extensive dental needs and must stay within their budget.

cc: Dr. Clarke Kent

Informed Consent

The Laws of Nature

Chapter eight shows how to structure informed consent as an important internal marketing tool and give the patient the most thorough understanding of the benefits, risks and alternatives to care. Nine specific issues of informed consent are discussed as well as how to implement financial contracts into the consent appointment. This chapter illustrates:

- The preoperative appointment—your best weapon against medical/legal scavengers
- How to preserve your rights in a hostile litigious environment
- How to create the most complete dental record any plaintiff's attorney has ever seen

Medical/legal issues are important in the business environment of the 1990s. Malpractice lawsuits provide the strongest incentives against advancement of our clinical skills and depletes the satisfaction with our careers.

The preoperative appointment is the final step in the no-contest case presentation. While the preoperative appointment involves no clinical treatment, it's of critical importance in the no-contest dentistry chain of events. During this business-orientated meeting with patients, you must complete the process of informed consent, confirm financial arrangements, and collect initial payment. It's wise to learn how to conduct the preoperative appointment successfully so you don't stumble on a source of contention and inadvertently start a contest with patients.

Preparation for the preoperative session actually begins during case discussion, when you supply patients with informational materials about their treatment and copies of consent forms to review at home. It's very important that patients have adequate time to look over all these materials. When appropriately presented, informed consent acts as a weapon against barriers in the mind. The time you spend with patients focusing on their needs as stipulated in the informed consent forms helps build rapport and inspires referrals.

Keep in mind that the preoperative appointment usually is the last opportunity you have to build value into the doctor/patient relationship prior to the beginning of treatment. Even thought the patient has indicated to you he or she is going ahead with care and may have made the down payment, the patient can still change his or her mind.

The value from patients' points of view within the preoperative appointment takes many forms. First, patients appreciate the extra time and care you are giving them, thus making them feel important. Next, all options, risks, and benefits of care are reinforced. They are given all the time and opportunity they need to feel safe. And third, you are ensuring they will not be embarrassed or angered about the financial obligations. Specific and firm financial arrangements are the best insurance against contests starting when treatment is completed.

A good informed consent model is the request for treatment form. I designed this form from the principles of informed consent from the ADA. The request for treatment form has nine areas.

1. I have requested treatment because . . . .

2. I understand my dental condition will be treated by the following means . . . .

3. The expected outcome (prognosis) of treatment is . . . .

4. If I elect not to have treatment, I understand the following may occur . . . .

5. I understand the condition can be treated in the following alternative methods . . . .

6. I understand the treatment recommended is recommended for me because it has the following advantages over the alternative methods of treatment . . . .

7. I understand the treatment planned, like all treatment, has some risks. The significant risks involved in my treatment have been explained to me and are . . . .

8. I understand the doctor may, on occasion, have visiting doctors and their staff observing procedures, and

that photographs may be taken during my treatment for use in clinical presentations, for which I give my permission.

9. I have been given time and opportunity to discuss this proposed treatment, alternatives, and risks with the doctor.

For each of these areas I write a short comment on the form, specific to the patient's case. You cannot delegate the informed consent process to a staff member. You must participate, using all the communication skills discussed in previous chapters to enhance the impact of your message and build patient confidence. It takes me about 15 minutes to complete this form, and it's been worth its weight in gold in clearing up misunderstandings before treatment has started.

Patients can't help but be impressed when they see how much time you're willing to spend with them, discussing and documenting all nine points on the consent form. They'll quickly realize that no doctor has ever been as thorough in preparing them for medical or dental care. Once again, you have positioned yourself as unique and have demonstrated outstanding value. What better way could there be to encourage referrals?

If you've followed the procedures for the no-contest case presentation, patients will barely bat an eyelash when you come to the financial agreement phase of the preoperative appointment. The financial contract patients sign during this appointment merely confirms in writing what has already been discussed and agreed to.

All you are asking is that patients verify their commitment.

When making financial arrangements with patients for reconstructive dentistry, ask either for full payment in advance or divide the fee into two or three installments, not to extend beyond completion of the final treatment. Remember, once patients have completed care, their priorities can shift. It's too easy to find reasons not to pay you after the work is done.

An important underlying objective of the preoperative appointment is to assemble the most complete dental record any plaintiff's attorney has ever seen. Dental malpractice suits generally focus on two issues: informed consent and standard of care. The standard of care issue is more subjective and may have to be decided by a court. The matter of informed consent, however, is more easily determined. Informed consent legal challenges usually vanish when you can produce proper consent forms that are signed and dated by patients who had adequate time and opportunity to discuss with you the benefits and risks involved in their care—and you have these events documented in the dental record.

Take this medical, legal, and financial preparation seriously. Even the most congenial patients can dramatically change their attitude toward you. It's naive to think patients will not sue you. Suits can also be instigated against you by patients' spouses, other relatives, former employees, other dentists, and state boards. The preoperative appointment is your best weapon against medical/legal scavengers. If you are building a career in reconstructive dentistry, it's a matter of when, not if, you will be sued. The preoperative appointment offers you an opportunity to plan accordingly. It's important you live within the laws of nature.

REQUEST FOR TREATMENT

I hereby request that treatment be provided for me as follows:

1. I have requested treatment because: _____

   _____

2. I understand that my dental condition will be treated by the following means:
   Upper: _____
   Lower: _____

3. The expected outcome of treatment (prognosis) is:
   Upper: _____
   Lower: _____

4. If I elect not to have treatment, I understand the following may occur:
   Upper: _____
   Lower: _____

5. I understand that the condition can be treated in the following alternative methods:
   Upper: _____
   Lower: _____

6. I understand that the treatment recommended is recommended because for me it has the following advantages over the alternative methods of treatment:

Upper: _____

Lower: _____

7. I understand that the treatment projected, like all treatment, has some risks. I know I have the right to know all possible risks just by asking. The significant risks involved in my treatment have been explained to me and are:

A. _____

B. _____

C. _____

D. _____

8. I understand that the doctor may on occasion have visiting doctors and their staff observing procedures, and that photographs may be taken during my treatment for use in clinical presentations for which I give my permission.

9. I have been afforded time and an opportunity to discuss this proposed treatment and alternatives and risks with the doctor.

Signature of
Patient or Guardian _____

Date _____

Signature of Witness_____

IMPLANT COMMENTS

Implant comments were a source of patient information regarding implant dentistry. A similar source can be created for any aspect of dentistry—cosmetics, orthodontics, periodontics. Patients experienced value when they realized the consent for care I was giving them was customized to their particular case and not a boiler-plate form everyone would sign.

This information source was given to the patient the appointment prior to the preoperative appointment. They would read it at home and return with questions. These questions formed the basis for the request for treatment form I discussed earlier in this chapter.

Purpose

This patient information monograph gives you as much information as we can in a convenient format. Write your questions in each page margin to enable us to present adequate information. However, if you have no questions about anything on the page, please sign on the line to let us know you read the page and understand it.

Natural Teeth

Your own natural teeth—in a healthy, well-maintained condition—are the best teeth you can possibly have. Nothing compares to them. The best interest of your health and well-being are served by doing everything you can to keep your teeth in the best condition as long as possible. With good self care and frequent dental checkups, you can accomplish this goal.

Supplementing Natural Teeth

When a tooth is lost, it's best to replace it with a nonremovable replacement as promptly as possible. With the replacement of a single tooth, a nonremovable bridge is often quite satisfactory. However, when replacing a number of missing teeth to restore chewing efficiency, you have to increase the support lost with the natural teeth. The artificial tooth of a bridge has no root. In reality, this is no great concern for a single tooth replacement. But, when two or three teeth in a row are lost, or several teeth spread out intermittently through the entire jaw, a considerable amount of root support has been lost. This makes a difference. In effect, we have increased the load on each remaining tooth because there are fewer of them. The loss can be compared to losing fence posts in a long fence. The fence is no shorter, but fewer posts comprise it. The fence is not as strong as before. More fence posts need to be added to increase overall strength. Similarly, weakened areas in the mouth need the aide of implants to replace missing root structures.

Partial Dentures

Does a removable partial denture replace the missing teeth as well as an implant? Partial dentures are either tooth-supported or tooth- and gum-supported. When entirely tooth-supported, the space has been replaced or filled in, but the supporting teeth remain the same. In other words, the load has been increased on the remaining teeth. In the case of a partial denture that is both tooth- and gum-supported, the number of teeth has not increased (there is still no more root support than before). The areas where teeth are missing have been filled in with gum-supported dentures. This means that the gum tissue and bone under these dentures will gradually shrink, and the partial denture will have to be remade or relined periodically. If these areas are not relined, a space develops under the denture. It is not bearing its fair share of the chewing load, and the remaining natural teeth are overworked. The teeth are overloaded. Under these conditions, the remaining teeth will undergo accelerated bone loss. Also this partial denture is removable; it is not permanently fastened like a nonremovable bridge is.

Tooth Supporting Bone

Nature has provided tooth-supporting bone for the years when teeth are present. When teeth are lost, the tooth-supporting bone degenerates. Nature takes away what you do not use! For example, a person confined to bed for a long time loses muscle tone. The muscles get soft and literally wither away. In the mouth, the bone under the gums "shrinks," and dentures get loose. Notice a person's mouth who has lost half his teeth; the bone is present around the remaining teeth. Where teeth have been lost, many times the bony ridge looks like a "sway-backed" horse. Where implants have been properly placed and maintained, the bone tends to be preserved since it is still being used.

Chewing Efficiency

To compare, let's assume a patient—with all his or her natural teeth in a healthy, well-maintained and func-tionally accurate condition—can chew at 100 percent efficiency. With every tooth lost, the amount of chew-ing efficiency decrease depends on whether or not the teeth are replaced and how. Ultimately, if all teeth are lost, he will have perhaps a 15 to 18 percent chewing efficiency (with good-fitting dentures on adequate bony ridges).

If the ridges are inadequate, the percentage decreases. With implants and nonremovable bridgework, or well-supported tooth replacement methods, he could realize as high as 85 percent efficiency, depending on the num-ber and condition of natural teeth.

Medical Examination

This is an absolute necessity! We will give you a Medical History Verification form for your physician. He or she will verify your general health and provide recent ex-amination results including blood tests and urinalysis.

He or she will indicate drug allergies and/or alternative recommendations. We want to be sure you are healthy and will heal nicely. We want your medical doctor aware of the treatment we plan and the medications we may prescribe.

Home Care

The dental care you provide yourself at home must be excellent. You must keep your teeth and implants cleaner than you may have before. You must be able to use a toothbrush, dental floss, or other devices we recommend to keep plaque off your teeth and implants. If not, there is a very good possibility that the implants will not succeed and will have to be removed. Smoking and excessive alcohol consumption deter excellent dental health as well.

X-Rays

You must have a complete examination with X-rays including a panoramic shot of your entire mouth. X-rays are necessary for proper diagnosis and treatment follow-up.

Opposing Teeth

The teeth or dentures in the arch opposite the implanted area are important to the success of the implant. There must be no grinding of the teeth at night (bruxism) against the implant. Care must also be taken not to overload the implant by chewing ice or hard objects that could damage even your natural teeth. The patient should not engage in fights or anything else that could damage the implant or underlying bone.

Loss of Nerve Sensation

Temporary loss of nerve sensation following certain surgical procedures has been reported in dental literature. This does happen sometimes, but is usually temporary.

Unfortunately, there have been instances where complete nerve sensation has not returned even after many years. Such occurrences have followed removal of deeply impacted wisdom teeth. Loss of feeling could happen with the placement of implants in the bone. A loss of nerve sensation is usually temporary and does not cause the face to droop or sag.

Are All Implants Successful?

No. Many variables must be considered in placing the implant. First, the patient must be healthy and possess adequate healing powers. An uncontrolled diabetic, for example, has less chance for healing, which could be quite a problem. If such a condition develops after the implant, failing health will certainly complicate the future of the implant. Second, accurate diagnosis must be made, and the proper implant selected and installed correctly. Third, it must be treated with care by the patient and the dentist. If either forgets diligent care, a problem may arise. Fourth, if the patient is a heavy smoker or an excessive alcoholic beverage user, the success of the implant will be affected for the worse.

Will Implants Last a Lifetime?

Every implant is placed with the expectation it will endure for the patient's life. With today's implant dentistry technology, a lifetime result is achievable.

Is Age a Deterrent?

No! Health is a deterrent. Many people 70 and 80 years of age are a better surgical risk than someone years younger in poor health. Older people are more likely to need implants because they have lost more teeth and ridge. As long as you live, you owe it to yourself, family and friends to take the best care of yourself you possibly can. Incidentally, what is a good age for a heart or kidney transplant or a coronary bypass? If you needed such an operation to stay alive or improve the quality or your life, would you refuse because of age?

Rejection by the Body?

Implants are made of biologically compatible materials extensively tested over several years in research laboratories using animals. Since these materials are largely metal, titanium, vitallium, etc., and have never been living tissue, there is no likelihood of an antigen-antibody response that could cause rejection similar to organ transplant rejection.

Can Implants Cause Cancer?

No reports in the dental literature indicate dental implants have ever been the cause of cancer.

How Is An Implant Inserted?

Although there are many types of implants, they can be divided into two basic groups: those inserted in the bone and those placed over the bone. In both instances, the implants are placed under the tissue, and extend through the mouth's tissue.

Decisions

If you want to be considered as an implant candidate, and feel no psychological problem will result if you have implants, you can take encouragement from the many successful hip transplants, kidney transplants, heart transplants and cornea transplants. If you do not feel you have adequate emotional stability to undergo similar treatment, then I would advise you against having an implant.

Guarantee

It is impossible for us to guarantee anything that goes into the mouth and under the patient's control. The physician doesn't tell you a transplanted heart or kidney, or a coronary bypass, will keep you alive for any specified period of time. We will endeavor to place the implant properly, to give you needed information on proper implant care at home, and to be available for regular periodic checkups to evaluate your continued dental health. We will do everything we can to make the implant succeed, and you will have to make the same commitment. If you do not hold up your end of the bargain you may experience problems. You must return to our office at regular intervals according to our recommendations for examination and service.

Cosmetic Surgery

Are dental implants inserted for cosmetics reasons? Absolutely not! The primary objective of dental implants is to give additional support to the replacement teeth. Dental implantology is not a total substitute for facelift plastic surgery. Some cosmetic enhancement is possible. Those expectations should be fully discussed prior to treatment.

Further Questions

If you have any questions not fully answered by this monograph, please feel free to ask them prior to beginning treatment. We will do our best to inform you.

Dealing with Failing Dentistry
The Call of the Wild

This chapter looks at the ethical/professional issues regarding replacing existing dentistry. Since most reconstructive dentistry is replacement dentistry, knowing how to communicate can reduce the awkward and uncomfortable situations that accompany telling patients their existing dentistry needs replacing. In this chapter we learn:

- What do you say to a patient with failing dentistry?
- Cannibalism in dentistry
- Why it's important to resist making treatment recommendations when you or the patient are upset

The reality of reconstructive dentistry is that it often needs revision and replacement. Part of preserving fee-for-service dentistry is putting retreatment into its proper perspective. Blaming the patient's previous dentist for poor work sets a bad example—if dentists don't respect dentists, why should patients?

If you do any type of extensive reconstructive dentistry, you know there's always the potential for technical and management failures. You've seen it happen. Patients in long-term periodontal maintenance programs give up trying to clean sensitive exposed root surfaces and impossible-to-reach furcations and eventually loose their teeth. Endodontically treated teeth with posts that serve as key abutments for fixed bridgework can split. Decay can form around extensive full-mouth reconstructions. Full and partial dentures of every configuration can become loose, sore, and broken.

The technical problems involved in failed dentistry, unfortunately, can be accompanied by management failures in the doctor/patient relationship. Because reconstructive dentistry almost always involves replacing previous dental work, it's imperative you know what to say to patients with failing dentistry. What you say about another dentist's failing dentistry says a lot about you. There's a simple, effective method for discussing this potentially explosive topic, whether it involves removing or replacing another dentist's work or your own. The only two necessary steps are 1) blame no one, and 2) look for solutions, not problems.

It's sad but true: Most dentists are trained to find fault. It's part of the learning process based on scientific cause-and-effect relationships. The logical approach, then, is to apply cause-and-effect thinking to the assessment of failing dentistry. Human nature, however, equates cause with blame—and there's the rub.

If a terminal abutment under a long-span fixed bridge fails, you might logically determine the cause as excessive loading. Your patient, however, twists that cause into blame. "Why didn't my previous dentist tell me this could happen? Why did he do this if he knew it could fail?" Patients often search for a person to blame. Unfortunately, too many dentists help them find it.

Blame is usually left to simmer at the feet of other dentists, or it is directed at patients themselves. Neither is healthy nor proper. Sometimes it's easy to pass judgment on another dentist's work, especially if you're working under the illusion that your work is perfect. Patients with failing dentistry are already disappointed and discouraged, so it's not hard to lead them down the path to find someone, preferably their previous dentist, to blame. It's also easy to blame patients for their own failed dentistry. Plaque is always a convenient scapegoat, as are missed recall appointments, poor diet and health habits, and noncompliance with treatment recommendations.

No-contest dentistry assigns no blame. Pointing the finger of blame is unhealthy for you, your patients, and the dental profession. It drags you down with it and labels your patients as victims. Assigning blame to colleagues attacks their professional reputation and sets in patients' minds the message that it's okay for dentists to blame one another. You don't do yourself any favors by blaming patients for their own failed dentistry either. All you're doing is setting up a contest that no one can win. If you say patients' dentistry failed because of something they did or didn't do, how can you guarantee your own work won't meet with the same result? Blame is a boomerang that will find you the first time your work fails.

Instead of assigning blame, ask yourself, "If I were responsible for this dentistry, what would I want my patient's next dentist to say about it?" When you adopt this attitude, you'll be amazed how many positive things you can find to say about a patient's condition.

Never make firm treatment recommendations when you or the patients are upset. Decisions made under such circumstances are rarely good ones. The no-contest format allows ample time for patients to calm down while they are warming up to you.

Before you begin any work on patients with failed dentistry, contact their previous dentist. You'll find he or she can offer valuable input and a new slant on exactly what happened in the relationship. If patients refuse to tell you the name of their previous dentist, do not initiate any rehabilitative procedures. Offer only relief from pain or infection until their anger has abated, and they're willing to cooperate.

In every discussion with patients suffering from failing dentistry, look for solutions instead of problems. This attitude opens everyone's mind to new possibilities. Apply the same technical skill, creativity, and insight necessary to perform reconstructive surgery to the communication process so you can talk to patients about replacing existing dentistry without cultivating ill will, anger, or stress. By focusing on solutions and refusing to assign blame, you'll be helping to preserve the integrity of the entire profession.

From 1981 to 1995, my practice was exclusively reconstructive dentistry. During that time I examined 15 to 40 new implant and reconstruction patients a month. I have seen just about every conceivable complication and failure related to dental care, including recurrent decay, open margins, poor occlusion, root fractures, split teeth, multiple fistulas, long-term undiagnosed periodontal disease, improper planes of occlusion, inadequate vertical dimension, and endodontic failures. I've also witnessed periodontal failures, prosthodontic failures, orthognathic relapse and failures, orthodontic failures, failed implants, fractured implants, oral/antral fistulas, fractures mandibles, parathesia, anathesia, hyperthesia, and facial trauma related to dental care. The list could go on. During 1981 to 1995 in *every* case where there was problem dentistry, I was able help my patients see and pursue solutions instead of seeing blame and pursuing litigation against their previous dentist. I was able to do it because I was willing to do it.

During that same period of time I have had many opportunities to act as an expert witness for dentist defendants. In every case I reviewed and participated in, there was an expert dentist witness for the plaintiff. In almost all cases (the exceptions were rare), the plaintiff's "expert" witness(es) had a motive for testifying that was not related to standard of care. The reasons included turf battles for specialty procedures between specialists and generalists; complete disregard for differences related to treatment approaches; strong low self-esteem issues; political agendas based on race, region of origin, attitudes on advertising; or the defendant dentist being too successful.

After 20 years of watching the actions of these so-called expert witnesses and listening to the gossip and character assassinations that occur among our colleagues, it is absolutely amazing to me that the offending predatory dentists don't realize they are engaging in a contest no one can win. Suing dentists does not improve the standard of care. Gossiping about your colleagues says more about you than it does about them. As many expert witnesses have discovered, instigating a lawsuit against a colleague has never brought more peace or prosperity into their practice or to the profession. There is a cannibalism occurring in dentistry. The act of preying on one's own has universally been regarded as the lowest form of behavior. Justifiably, these experts often find out the hard way there is a high price for the need to be right.

CASE PRESENTATION FOR RETREATMENT

One of the most awkward and uncomfortable situations you'll encounter in dentistry is discovering technical problems with your own work and presenting options for retreatment to patients. As unpleasant as it is, this scenario is also your best guide to handling the failing work of other dentists.

Let's look again at Mrs. Leonard who now has heavy plaque and recurrent decay under a key abutment and periapical radiolucencies showing in two restored teeth. Root fractures have also occurred on teeth you endodontically restored with posts and fixed prosthetics. At least three-fourths of her original reconstructive work, which four years ago cost $18,000, needs to be remade. What do you say to her?

First, acknowledge the problem. It's your ethical obligation to inform patients as soon as you are aware of a problem. Present clinical facts without any reference to whose fault it might be. Don't blame the patients, yourself, the laboratory. Blame no one. Express genuine concern over the problem but do not justify or apologize. Stay calm and emotionally in control.

"Mrs. Leonard, I'm concerned about some tooth decay I see around the edges of your crowns. There also appears to be some broken teeth and infection present. I'm going to take a few more X-rays to determine the status of these areas. Is that all right with you?"

Mrs. Leonard may say, "I don't understand. I just had this work done a few years ago, and now you're telling me I've got more problems. Why did this happen?"

A good reply would be, "I'm concerned, too, Mrs. Leonard. Let me make these X-rays, and I'll study your case. We can talk next time about what we need to do. Is that okay?"

Don't let the who's-to-blame contest ever get started. It's certainly a contest no one can win. If patients blame you for their failing dentistry, do not argue. Acknowledge the problem, express your concern, and offer to study the situation so you can make recommendations based on facts. Never offer solutions or make treatment recommendations when you or your patients are upset.

Next, review the case carefully. Schedule patients for X-rays or other diagnostic studies as needed. Emphasize the need to be comprehensive in your approach to the problem.

The third step in discussing your failed dentistry is to review treatment recommendations. Discuss repair options within the context of your patient's budget, just as you would in any initial no-contest case review. Don't shake at the knees when you tell patients you are going to charge them for replacing their dentistry. All the rules for determining a budget apply to retreatment situations. Most people recognize that failures can occur and are reasonable in discussions. It's when patients think you're blaming them for the failure that they become combative.

Do not assign or accept blame. Offer a specific solution. After you have carefully studied diagnostic materials and your patient has the right attitude, present a retreatment solution within the patient's stated budget.

Finally, follow the steps of informed consent. The informed consent process is just as important, if not more so, the second time around. There's no guarantee that replacement dentistry will last forever, and patients need to recognize that fact—in writing.

If you observe these steps, you'll find most patients to be cooperative, reasonable, and grateful that you haven't blamed them for their dental problems. It's the small percentage of unreasonable people who are at the center of most stress related to patient management.

There's nothing you can do to change some people's attitudes. The best you can do is make dealing with them tolerable over the length of your career. Blaming them, hating them, or staying angry with them only reduces the quality of your own life and dilutes energy that could be given to positive life experiences. The best advice I can give to an aspiring reconstruction dentist is to learn to lay down your frustration and walk away. You're not punished *for* your anger, you are punished *by* it.

Comparative Anatomy

of Traditional and "No-Contest" Case Presentations

Chapter 10 compares the no-contest case presentation with the traditional approach of case presentation. Chief among the differences between the no-contest style and the traditional style is the direct approach used to determine the patient's budget. Other differences include timing of hygiene and diagnostic materials and how treatment options are presented. This chapter also points out:

- Inherited vs. acquired traits of case presentation—what you have been taught vs. what you have learned
- How and why your financial comfort affects treatment planning
- Different species of dentists

Preserving fee-for-service dentistry means looking for new ways to advance our profession. The traditional case presentation is no longer adequate in a clinical environment with increasing fees, time in treatment, and risks.

Every appointment you have with patients is a case presentation appointment. No matter what activity is occurring, you want patients to experience value, which in turn builds confidence, satisfaction, loyalty, and trust. The no-contest approach fulfills these requirements and represents a new way of looking at dental practice management.

The no-contest case presentation differs from the more traditional one in several key areas. While each method has six fundamental steps, the objectives—and, therefore, the results—may vary greatly.

The steps in the no-contest case presentation can be accomplished in a few office appointments or extended over many years. Under ideal conditions, the order of no-contest appointments and their management objectives looks like this:

1. Initial Interview and Examination
   Management Objective—Introduce the concept of a lifetime strategy for dental health.

2. Diagnostic Records
   Management Objective—Introduce budget.

3. Case Review
   Management Objective—Confirm budget.

4. Case Discussion
   Management Objective—Recommend treatment that fits within budget.

5. Case Review Letter
   Management Objective—Repeat that position of practice is unique.

6. Preoperative
   Management Objective—Ensure medical/legal
   protection.

The traditional style of presenting care follows a different sequence:

1. Initial Hygiene (Prophylaxis) Appointment
   Management Objective—Create a favorable first
   impression.

2. Initial Interview, Examination and Diagnostic
   Record
   Management Objective—Create a favorable second impression.

3. Case Presentation
   Management Objective—Recommend treatment
   and fee.

4. Negotiation
   Management Objective—Present alternative treatment plans within budget and discuss insurance.

5. Renegotiation
   Management Objective—Recommend treatment
   alternatives within budget.

6. Preoperative
   Management Objective—Ensure medical/legal
   protection.

From the very first step, the two approaches—the traditional and the no-contest—differ in form and function, in content and purpose. In most general practitioners offices that use the traditional model, new patients are

commonly seen first by a hygienist. This initial appointment is not treated as part of the case presentation but
simply as a way to deliver routine hygiene services, create a favorable first impression, and encourage patients
to seek needed care. Difficulties can arise early, however.

Aside from the medical, legal, and safety issues raised
by assigning initial patient contact to a hygienist, the
traditional form opens the door for an immediate contest. Dental hygienists are trained to spot problem areas
in patients' mouths, but when they point out trouble
areas and suggest solutions, they unknowingly start a
contest.

Most patients needing rehabilitative care have complex
dental problems with embarrassing psychological and
financial components. It's not likely these patients, the
majority of whom are over age 50, will feel comfortable
discussing their concerns with a usually young hygienist.

Reread the section on the value of patient education in
Chapter 6.

More compelling, however, are differences in the two
methods regarding treatment recommendations and
budget. Under the traditional case presentation plan,
budget is determined by trial and error.

Dentists make treatment recommendations (trial) and
patients refuse them (error) until the cost of recommended treatment meets patients' budgets. Sometimes
practitioners use the multiple treatment plan approach,

offering up a Sears and Roebuck catalog of optional treatment plans with high, higher, and highest fees attached.

These indirect methods of determining a patient's budget require extensive technical explanations with supporting study models, photographs, drawings, and lots of hot air. Talking too much invites overselling and does nothing to scale barriers in the mind. Having patients chose their own treatment plan can make you appear indecisive and lacking in confidence. Patients come to you because you are supposed to be the expert. It is of no value to the patient if you force them to decide their treatment plan.

Many dentists have been taught to put the responsibility of choosing the treatment plan on the patient. What these same dentists will eventually learn is patients respond to leadership. Leadership is not taught in dentistry. You can learn leadership in private fee-for-service practice if you let your patients teach you. They teach you leadership by accepting treatment plans that are offered in a confident manner and reject ones that are contaminated with indecision.

Traditional case presentations thrive on negotiation and compromise, while the no-contest form tries never to have anything to negotiate about. Patients and practitioners save time, thought, effort, and emotional issues when the dental budget is approached early and directly in the case presentation process. Once budget is determined, everyone's full efforts can be directed into a single treatment plan, one that will take patients as far into their lifetime strategy as possible.

DO YOUR HOMEWORK

Certain prerequisites are fundamental to the success of no-contest dentistry. Mechanically following the six steps in the process will rarely lead to success without prior preparation in key areas including clinical competence, communication skills, financial goals, and life purpose.

Clinical competence drives diagnosis and treatment planning of complex dentistry. To function effectively, you need to be comfortable with and knowledgeable in all phases of treatment, although you may not perform all aspects of care. Referrals for specialty procedures are both wise and appropriate within the scheme of no-contest dentistry. Just make sure that all other dentists treating your patient understand and reinforce the importance of the lifetime dental health strategy and pledge to respect the budget.

Clinical competence also requires an ability to manage complications and failures that can occur in complex dentistry. Fear of failure can shortchange patients if it keeps you from presenting appropriate, comprehensive treatment. It limits your therapeutic range and may ultimately stunt your personal and professional growth. By accepting occasional failure as a reality of dentistry, you are more likely to deliver dentistry that succeeds.

Strong communication skills are another vital prerequisite. Many dentists, however, confuse communication with lecturing. Resist the temptation to pad case presentations with lengthy discussions, hand-drawn diagrams, stacks of before- and-after photographs, and imposing models of dental hardware. For true communication to occur, the message must not only be heard, but understood. Case presentations that go on too long and are too technical leave you talking to yourself.

High-impact communication is not content-specific; it's knowing how to listen. Patients are much more likely to understand case review discussions when you skillfully blend *what* you say with *when* and *how* you say it. Tone of voice and body language carry your message more than the meaning of the words you use. And, like it or not, high-impact communication has nothing to do with your ability to fix teeth.

One of the most common stumbling blocks to providing no-contest dentistry is cash flow. When finances are tight, it may appear more expedient to jump right into providing care during the initial appointment, rather than leading patients step-by-step through the no-contest process.

Don't confuse the patient's ability to pay with your own. It only adds to barriers in the mind (see Chapter 1). Few dentists are comfortable offering dentistry that is beyond their own ability to pay. True financial comfort is a blend of economics and philosophy. One person's ceiling is another person's floor. The production and net income level that delights one dentist could emotionally cripple another. Be realistic as well as confident in determining your own comfort level. Having a regular savings plan, current accounts payable, healthy accounts receivable, and reasonable overhead should provide sufficient incentive to implement no-contest dentistry.

WHAT'S THE PURPOSE?

Having a clearly defined purpose in life makes all the difference in how you approach the practice of dentistry. Purpose is the single, unifying theme and underlying motivation for everything you do in your personal life as well as your profession. It answers the question, "Why practice dentistry?"

You can approach the question from numerous perspectives. First, dentistry can be viewed as a job, as a means of providing food, shelter, and safety. When dentistry is a job, the connection between income and expense becomes a major focus. People and events that contribute to profitability are defined as good; those that interrupt work flow or cherished management systems are bad, producing problems and stress.

For no-contest dentistry to succeed under such a perspective, apply the brakes. Rushing to provide rehabilitative treatment for patients during the first or second appointment may fulfill a "fast, friendly service" office motto and momentarily bolster your bottom line, but it does little to link patients to your practice through a lifetime. Many patients may need time to recognize and appreciate the value available in your practice.

Dentistry can also be viewed as a mission, its purpose being to help and please people. The focus for this type of approach is building and keeping harmony in relationships. People and events that contribute to peace and accord are defined as good. Confrontations that disrupt relationships are bad.

Treatment planning is the key for successfully introducing no-contest dentistry in this type of setting. Don't be hesitant to recommend complex, rehabilitative care for fear patients will be upset about its cost. Dentists who see their practice as a mission often enjoy long, engaging conversations with patients, but they avoid any mention of potentially upsetting money issues.

Perhaps you look at dentistry as an adventure, a creative expression of imagination. Dentist adventurers focus on change. People and events that interrupt work flow aren't viewed as obstacles, but as challenges. Adventurers like to try new techniques and tools, take more risks, and are less likely to stick to a prescribed plan—preferring to tinker with the process just to see how it works. Adventurers are comfortable only as long as their actions are inventive and spark growth.

In their enthusiasm, adventurers see rehabilitative dentistry as an adventure for their patients, too. Treatment failures and medical or legal issues are just part of the experience. They see themselves as guides, leading patients through uncharted treatment waters, meeting all challenges, and fixing all problems.

If this is your approach, you'll eagerly embrace no-contest dentistry because it's new and presents a challenge. Resist the temptation, however, to tinker with it. Concentrate on the process and be consistent in implementation. Showcasing organization and efficiency, especially in early appointments, builds trust so that if you do deviate from the format, patients are willing to follow.

There is nothing wrong with viewing dentistry as a job, a mission, or an adventure. There are different species of dentists. It's been my experience that most dentists see their profession from a combination of overlapping perspectives—the job, the mission, and the adventure—with a single area being dominant. The important factor is recognizing what your perspective is and how its purpose can enhance or interfere with the concept of no-contest dentistry.

There is no one right way to look at the practice of dentistry. Technical quality, patient satisfaction, and personal fulfillment are all achievable no matter how you view it. Ultimately, your predominant attitude toward dentistry is a product of how you view yourself.

The Team Approach to Case Presentation

Is There Safety in Numbers?

Our next chapter walks you through case presentation for patients treated in a referral relationship. The greatest reasons for failure of the team approach are the conflicting messages the patient hears from each office. Learn about:

- Dental office symbiosis and the roles of each office within the team approach
- How to harness the power of third party endorsement
- High impact referral procedures

The team approach to reconstructive care is growing more popular. Our advantage in preserving fee-for-service dentistry is leveraged when two or more offices demonstrate true cooperation.

Reconstructive dentistry is often accomplished within a team approach, the team being generalists and specialists working together with hygienists, laboratory technicians, nurse anesthetists, preventative therapists, and support staff. The no-contest case presentation functions wonderfully within the team approach when all the members are aware of the communication principles behind the concepts of the no-contest process.

The team members involved in reconstructive dentistry can all practice within one office or in multiple locations. Teams located in one office usually are configured as owners and associates, partners, or solo practitioners sharing expenses. Usually, these teams are composed of general practitioners. Teams located in multiple locations usually are general practitioners and specialists working together in traditional referral relationships.

Over the last few years, more single-office location teams of generalists and specialists are developing. General practices are hiring specialists to perform specialty procedures in their office. An emerging trend in team building involves the speciality practices hiring general practitioners and restorative dentists to provide prosthetic dentistry.

The one-office team approach to reconstructive care offers the advantages in optimizing the impact of communication, providing value, and minimizing fragmentation of care. For 15 years I practiced reconstructive dentistry in this fashion. I have had both associates and solo practitioners sharing expenses. Team members were general practitioners, specialists, and nurse anesthetists.

My experience with associate general dentists within my practice of reconstructive care has been excellent. From 1979 to 1995, I employed six full- or part-time general dentist associates (one associate at a time), three specialists and two nurse anesthetists. We structured the team approach to reconstructive care to offer the patient the greatest value and give each team member the opportunity to work to his or her strengths.

I was responsible for all the adult new patient examinations as well as the subsequent treatment plans and consultations. On reconstruction patients, I did all of the periodontal and implant surgery as well as tooth extractions. I did the initial tooth preparations and established the anterior guidance, planes of occlusion, vertical dimension, and phonetics. These guidelines were established in the temporary restorations, and I made the necessary adjustments to them until patients were comfortable functionally, aesthetically, and phonetically.

My associates completed the final tooth preparations, made impressions, fit castings, tried in-bisque bake crowns and seated the final restorations. Of course, the amount of dentistry my associates provided for my reconstructive patients depended on their experience, willingness to learn, and patient preferences. I checked the critical steps they performed. After a few years together, our standards of care became more equal, and most of the restorative work they performed they did completely independent of me.

Patient management with this style of team approach was not difficult. After I completed the consultation process and the patient was ready for care, I would introduce my associate to the patient and explain that he would be a cotherapist in the case. At that point my associate would sit down with the patient and review his role. Over many years of using associates as cotherapists, very few patients had strong objections. I simply told those who did I would be happy to do all their work myself. I did not create a contest. Most patients, however, saw the value—they saved time and money. To be sure patients didn't feel abandoned to the associate, I kept in close contact with their case as it progressed. Short conversations with them during the appointment reassured them they were still "my" patient.

My experience with this team approach to care was excellent. It created several important advantages for the team and the patients. From the point of view of the patients, they received complete dental care in one location with the same familiar faces around them. This benefit offered tremendous value when they compared their treatment experiences with their friends who complained about traveling "all over town" to get their teeth fixed. Patients had only one place to go and one person to complain to (me) when things did not go as they expected. It provided value when they had their complaints heard and acted upon. Patients believed there was a single doctor in charge (me) and that everyone on the team knew their case.

There are significant benefits for the doctors within the team approach style. The support of the associates gave me time and energy to focus on the rigors of rehabilitative care. A big mistake I see many of my colleagues make is trying to treat too wide a patient mix—children in one chair, endodontics in another, and rehabilitation patients in the consultation room. Reconstructive dentistry requires focus. Too many different demands dilute the focus.

The two associates who made the greatest impact on our practice and who were with us the longest were Dr. John Fish and Dr. Randall Cline. Both were important assets.

Doctors Fish and Cline managed the general care side of our practice and helped many patients upgrade their dental health to complete care. Looking back on my relationship with these doctors, having a well-managed general care aspect of our practice was one of the single greatest assets to enabling me to build my reconstructive practice. By having associates who could run a general practice well, our overall practice provided "one-stop shopping" for the dental consumer.

Both of these doctors had patient and staff management styles that were different from my own. Reconstructive dentistry frequently creates patient and staff management challenges. If I was ineffective with a patient or staff member, my associates often could resolve the issues. Having different personalities available to manage and communicate is an important aspect of value for the patients, doctors, and staff.

Both Doctors Cline and Fish had the opportunity to participate in full-mouth rehabilitative care. The experiences they had in our office served as a foundation for both doctors to eventually build quality rehabilitative practices of their own.

The no-contest style of patient management evolved during the time they were with me. I was able to duplicate this style of team approach with subsequent associates as well. Yes, there were some problems. There were remakes, and some patients left the practice. But these things occur in a solo practice as well. The advantages of using the team approach for me, the patients, and the associates involved far outweighed the problems.

Much of the consulting I currently do is working with a referral base of specialists to whom I teach the concepts of no-contest dentistry. Based on extensive personal experiences in all areas of the country, I have learned that the team approach to dentistry fails most often because the patient is receiving conflicting messages. There is no safety in numbers when each office doesn't know what the other is doing.

Here's a typical situation: The new patient comes into the generalist's office. He examines the patient and concludes implants may be the best way to go to replace the missing posterior teeth. He tells the patient this following the examination and recommends she see an oral surgeon or periodontist for implant evaluations.

The patient, not quite sure of what is going on, begins to ask questions. As you can guess, this question-and-answer format escalates into the familiar "You have the problem, and I'll sell you the solution" scenario.

If the generalist is lucky, the patient will take his advice and seek the opinion of the specialist. Following the examination, the specialist starts the contest with the patient by detailing the technical steps of placing implants, giving the patient informed consent materials, and scheduling a CAT scan. Just as the specialist is ready to escort the patient out the door, the patient asks the knock-out question, "How much will my insurance pay for this work?"

"Didn't your general dentist explain all this to you?" the specialist gropes.

"No, the only thing he did was send me here, and I'm not sure I can afford all this. How much does a reline cost?"

Sound familiar? It probably does if you've been practicing the team approach. The no-contest process works fine within the team approach to care. Keep in mind that we should focus on providing value at every opportunity. The challenge within the team approach is to provide the perception of value as a team. It's value to which patients say "yes." Treatment within the team approach is the easy part.

Here are the steps.

1. The initial interview, examination, and post-examination discussion are exactly the same as before. The

objective is to introduce the concept of the lifetime strategy for dental health. No details of treatment alternatives are given or statements concerning referrals made.

2. The diagnostic records appointment in the team approach has two major management objectives. As before, the prime objective is to introduce the concept of budget. Remember the phrase, "Have you thought about your budget?" The second objective is to introduce the concept of referral. Here's how to do it. After introducing the idea of a budget, introduce the possibility of referral.

"Mrs. Leonard, as I study your case I may decide at some point to get a second opinion concerning replacing your missing teeth. You and I still have some work to do together, but I wanted you to know that this is an option open to us."

Don't make this a potential referral issue a big deal. Just introduce it. Remember, we're foreshadowing the referral if we need it the future. We want no surprises—and no contests with the patient.

3. The records review appointment is when the general dentist confirms the budget and recommends only that part of treatment that coincides with the budget. Every treatment team member should have a good idea what each other's fees are.

If I'm the general dentist and have planned three implants for Mrs. Leonard, I should know the ballpark fee for those implants, even though I'm not doing them. When Mrs. Leonard tells me her budget, I will automatically know whether implants are in the cards for her this year. If her budget is appropriate, this is the time I make the referral.

Let's look at this approach from the patient's point of view. It's now her third appointment. She's had a chance to build a relationship with you and your staff, and if you haven't started any contests, you're in pretty good shape in the patient's eyes.

You've discussed and confirmed her budget before you offered your treatment recommendations. Additionally, you mentioned before that a referral might be an option. From the patient's perspective, there have been no surprises.

Here's a good way to make the referral. I learned this from my personal physician, Dr. Charles Furree. Several years ago I had a routine physical for health insurance. The nurse at Dr. Furee's office just completed taking my 12-lead EKG. I was putting my shirt back on when Dr. Furee entered the room and said the words you fear the most just following an EKG, "I don't want to worry you, but . . . "

As it turned out, I had an anomaly to my atrial rhythm. Dr. Furree wanted a second opinion. He said, "I'm going to refer you to Dr. Chambers, a cardiologist here in Charlotte. Don't let his relative youth concern you when you meet him. He's one of Charlotte's best. All the old physicians go to him."

Dr. Furee then picked up the phone, speed-dialed Dr. Chambers office, got his scheduler, handed me the phone, and said, "Here, make your appointment." I thought, "Wow, now that was a referral!"

Since then, that's how I make my referrals. I dial the number in the consultation area in front of the patient. I tell the scheduler I have developed a lifetime strategy for dental health for Mrs. Leonard, and I'd like Dr. Salvin to evaluate her for implants. Then I hand the phone to Mrs. Leonard. She may not be able to schedule immediately, but the specialist's office can now get her name and address and send her registration information and a map to their office.

4. Before Mrs. Leonard arrives at the specialist's office, the generalist should communicate three things to the specialist. First, this patient is pursuing a lifetime strategy for dental health. Second, this patient has an annual budget of X dollars. And third, tell the specialist what the budgeted treatment plan is and the total treatment plan. All this can easily be done with a fax machine. Don't make the mistake of allowing Mrs. Leonard to show up at the specialist's office without these three items in place.

When Mrs. Leonard arrives at the specialist's office, he or she should reinforce the concept of the lifetime strategy for dental health. For example, "It's nice to meet you, Mrs. Leonard. I see you're referred from Dr. Grind's office and are interested in a lifetime strategy for dental health. Welcome to our office."

Specialists need to make it obvious that they and the generalist are communicating about Mrs. Leonard. Most patients believe it's easier to get doctors to use each other's toothbrushes than it is to get them to talk to one another.

Specialists should have everything they need to confirm the diagnosis of the generalist. After the examination, the specialist confirms to the patient that she can be helped with the procedure and it will be within her budget. The specialist must respect the budget. If there is a fundamental disagreement about the overall treatment plan, discuss it during a private conversation between doctors. *Don't* use the patient as the messenger.

Give the patient the necessary forms related to consent and financial arrangements and set an appointment with your office for any diagnostic work. Then refer her back to the generalist's office for the preoperative appointment.

5. The case review letter is generated from the generalist's office with reference to the care that will be provided by the specialist. Be sure to send a copy of this letter to the specialist.

6. The preoperative appointment should also reflect harmony between treating offices. Your financial arrangements, insurance procedures, and informed consent forms should resemble each other. Contests will start if one office offers payment plans and the

other requires cash in advance. Both offices should have a formal consent appointment as discussed earlier in this program.

No-contest dentistry within the team approach requires practice. It means specialists and generalists getting together and rehearsing the communication management between their offices. There is tremendous power in third party endorsement. Each office needs to endorse the other.

Third party endorsement is important between referring offices. There are three steps to follow. First, acknowledge the referring doctor as an expert in her area.

Next, say why she is an expert. Give proof. For example, "Mrs. McBucks, Dr. Davis is one of the best dentists in the area. I've worked with her for many years and she takes excellent care of her patients."

Finally, compliment the decision of the patient for selecting the referring doctor as her dentist. "Mrs. McBucks you made a wise decision choosing Dr. Davis as your dentist." The entire staff of both offices need to participate. Sound impossible? Unfortunately, it is for many treatment teams. They spend their time and money training themselves on dental techniques and ignore management and business courses.

The irony is that without great sales techniques, technical training amounts to nothing more than expensive entertainment for the doctor if patients don't agree to treatment. Remember, the team approach to dentistry fails most often because the patient is receiving conflicting messages from team members. The team approach is a great way to practice. Make it a no-contest environment putting all members of the team on the same side.

Yes and Know

Recognizing
Buying Behavior

Chapter 12 teaches how to recognize signals of acceptance and rejection from the patient during case presentation. This chapter shows:

- Learning to take "yes" for an answer
- Why overselling creates barriers to case acceptance
- What to do when patients say "no"

Many of the issues surrounding saving fee-for-service care relate to communicating its benefits to our patients. The chapter reinforces the importance of having solid and consistent communication skills.

Communication, by definition, is a two-way street. It's vital that in your rush to polish your own interpersonal techniques you don't overlook message cues from your patients. Their vocabulary, like yours, is not limited to words. Body language, physical appearance, and tone of voice account for the largest, most significant portion of the communications package. Consequently, patients may be saying "yes" or "no" to treatment recommendations long before you hear anything. For no-contest dentistry to succeed, it's important to recognize these messages and respond accordingly.

WHEN PATIENTS SAY "YES"

During discussions, do your patients lean forward to ask or answer questions? Do they look you in the eye? Without a word, these people are telling you, "yes." Respect the nonverbal clues and move on. Stop selling dentistry at the earliest possible moment.

If you continue to describe the benefits of treatment long after patients have indicated acceptance, you risk reminding them of past experiences with the "You have a problem, I'll sell you the solution" formula for case presentation, thus fortifying barriers in their minds. Overselling irritates patients and wastes everyone's time.

Overreacting to positive responses can also breed disastrous results. If patients have already indicated, verbally or otherwise, that they're willing to accept treatment, don't throw a party. Stop extolling the virtues of excellent dental health, put down the racks of slides, skip further testimonies from satisfied patients, and resist the desire to call in the entire staff for a celebration. While you're basking in the moment, patients may be asking, "Do these people really need my acceptance to make them feel good? Am I the only one who has agreed to this treatment?" Overselling calls attention to case presentations that are just selling jobs.

Knowing when to say when is the key response to patients who say "yes." The no-contest presentation process is designed to make it easy for them to respond positively. When they do, accept that you and your staff have done things right and move on to the next step. Learn to take "yes" for an answer.

WHEN PATIENTS SAY "NO"

Patients say "no" to treatment recommendations in as many ways as they say yes. They may fold their arms across their chest, knot their hands into a fist, gaze at the floor, or continually shift positions. They may veil a negative response by saying they've changed their mind. They may appear to accept your recommendations, but then never call back—except to have their records sent to another office!

Faced with feelings of rejection and frustration, you'll want to pout, "Why me? After all the continuing education I've had, all the hard work I've put into sharpening my skills, how can these people just walk away?" "Why me?" is the wrong question to ask when things don't go the way you prefer. It implies you're a victim. "Why me?" is the question to ask when things go *well*.

The proper response to patients who say "no" is, "Now what?" There are things you can do that may not win back individual patients, but will add to your knowledge and experience to make sure the process goes more smoothly in the future.

As soon as you discover a patient is lost, contact him or her by phone. *You* have to do it, not your office manager or receptionist. A good dialogue to follow is, "Hello, Mrs.

Leonard, this is Dr. Moneycut. I understand you have some questions about your care. How can I help you?"

You've now opened the door to discuss what's really going on with patients. Because there's some safety in distance, patients tend to be more frank over the telephone than they would be in a face-to-face meeting. Many times you'll be able to clear up a simple misunderstanding and ease them back to your office for care.

Next, write a letter summarizing your telephone conversation. If patients have decided to postpone treatment, enter their names and a recall date in your lost patient recovery system. (Keep patients in the recall system for a year before labeling their files inactive.)

Don't let those who decline treatment recommendations add bricks to the barriers in your mind. Step back from your frustration and look at the big picture. Chances are good that if you treated these people with dignity, didn't try to sell them a solution, and were nonjudgmental when they refused care, they'll ultimately return.

Reject the old myths that focus on perfection: "Patients won't refuse your care if you are a quality dentist." Or, "Treat people right and they won't leave your practice." Nothing is further from the truth. It's quite normal for people to leave dental practices for reasons unrelated to the quality of care they received or how they were treated. Patients lose jobs, move, divorce, marry, or take long expensive vacations they can't afford. Their priorities change. To get a proper perspective, ask yourself if you'd rather sit in a dental chair having your teeth ground down to the pulp, or go skinny-dipping in the South Pacific? It's not a hard decision.

There are many things you can do to keep patients saying "yes," but don't bet your mental health on any of them happening all the time.

Mental Health Strategies

Survival of the Fittest

This final chapter is about the mental preparation needed for practicing reconstructive dentistry. Like athletic competitions, visualizations along with healthy self-esteem, pride and an attitude of abundance prepare us for the rigors of providing excellent dental care. *Preserving fee-for-service dentistry means, above all, preserving the fee-for-service dentist.* This chapter demonstrates:

- Why high self-esteem and an attitude of abundance are prerequisites for case acceptance
- The illusion of private practice
- How to provide unconditional value

Whether or not your patients accept your treatment plans in a fee-for-service environment depends on your willingness to provide unconditional value. Patients will accept your care if they perceive you are uniquely qualified.

Have you ever walked into a case presentation when your mind was somewhere else—far, far away? Do worries about other things happening in your professional or personal life clog your brain just when it should be at its sharpest? Perhaps an unpleasant experience with another patient has contaminated your attitude. Or maybe the whole case presentation process causes you anguish. Mental stress can seriously inhibit your ability to relate successfully to patients on a no-contest basis. Before you can put the techniques of no-contest dentistry into practice, you must be psychologically and emotionally prepared. There are many mental health strategies that can insure your survival. I can assure you that the concepts of reconstructive dentistry and the "Survival of the Fittest" go hand in hand.

Although rehabilitative dentistry shouldn't be a contest, you can train for it like you would for an athletic competition. As all successful athletes recognize, the first, crucial step in developing mental and physical toughness is preparation. Rehabilitative dentistry requires you to be at the top of your game consistently, no matter what the circumstances. Confidence, then, is the key to mental preparation. If you don't have full confidence in your abilities, you won't get far. The best way to develop that confidence is to keep expanding your technical range of skills through continuing education and training.

The fundamental technical skill is knowing what you're treating. It's also imperative to stay healthy and physically fit. Rehabilitative dentistry requires superior hand/eye coordination and fine motor skills that can only be maintained by rigorous conditioning. Poor physical conditioning shows up most often in long afternoon appointments.

The link between mental and physical health is well documented. A focused, confident mental attitude contributes to physical health and well-being. When you display discipline in your attitude toward psychological and physical health, you're also setting an important example for patients and staff to model.

Healthy self-esteem is the foundational mental health concept of rehabilitative dentistry. It tells your patients they deserve and will receive your best efforts. One way to help build self-esteem is to visualize yourself as a champion. Before every case presentation, close your eyes and paint a mental picture of yourself as a winner. See that large, golden trophy with your name on it. Hear the crowd's applause and tell them, "Form a line here if you trust and love me." Then see yourself first in line. It may seem silly at first, but keep doing it. Before long, you'll be a believer—and your own biggest fan!

Sound too pompous? Not at all. Inner peace and self-love are actually the two greatest qualities needed in the practice of rehabilitative dentistry. Everything else falls into place when you're content with yourself and confident in your own abilities. Personal mastery and technical excellence are the by-products of self-love.

One of the most interesting characteristic of self-confidence is that it attracts that quality in others. Patients who suffer from poor self-esteem will be more likely to oppose you and your recommendations. They may consider you cocky or conceited. Your self-confident attitude will only remind them of their own shortcomings in that area, and they'll dislike you for it. Individuals with healthy self-esteem, however, will sense your positive self-concept and respect you for it. Consequently, they make the best candidates for rehabilitative dentistry and the most vocal referral sources.

VISUALIZE SUCCESS

An important rule for the successful practice of dentistry, or any endeavor, is to be proud of what you do. Consider that rehabilitative dentistry requires a master's hand—and mind. When you approach a case presentation, be proud of what you do. Visualize this as your finest moment. Hear the voices of appreciation around you. Enter with the confidence that you have the ability to meet this patient's needs. Assume you a have gift. Use it. Be proud of it.

A self-concept that includes abundance is another key element in developing a hardy mental attitude. Like self-esteem, it grows over time. A sense of abundance begins by realizing that happiness and fulfillment come from what you bring to dentistry, not what you get from it. This must be a conscious decision. The more you share an attitude of abundance, the more people will be drawn to it and to you.

The concept of abundance affects how you deal with money issues. If you see your practice as furnishing enough financial reward for you, you'll experience very little anxiety quoting fees to patients. When you visualize your patients as having enough money to pay for rehabilitative dentistry, you'll feed their self-confidence rather than make them feel inadequate or threatened.

Always assume patients have an attitude of abundance. If the fees you quote are within their budget, they'll write a check and treatment can begin. If the fees you quote don't fit their budget, patients with an attitude of abundance will opt for treatment that does.

Beware of patients who exhibit an attitude of lack. For them, any fee is threatening, regardless of their ability to pay. Supposedly rich people can also have an attitude of lack and are very unsuitable candidates for rehabilitative dentistry. They'll always find a way to become a victim by constantly reminding you how much they've paid, how much time and hassle they've experienced, and how much they've sacrificed. These people will never be totally satisfied with your care, regardless of its quality.

If you display an attitude of lack yourself, you'll never have the confidence to propose comprehensive care and a lifetime strategy for dental health. Your treatment plans will be based on what you assume patients can afford or on what you can afford. Planning treatment on assumptions of what people can pay is risky because you may not be offering patients the best, most appropriate care for their specific case. Ethically, who should determine the limits of dental care—doctors or patients? Do you plan treatment that's best for patients, or that's most comfortable for you to quote?

Nothing brings out an attitude of lack more quickly than the issue of dental insurance. It tempts patients, regardless of their ability to pay, to limit the scope of their dental care to the parameters of their dental insurance coverage. Insurance can also be a convenient scapegoat, producing in you an attitude that asks, "How can my patients get the care they need if insurance companies won't pay for it?" The real roadblock to comprehensive dental care isn't insurance coverage. It's an attitude of lack.

THE ILLUSION OF PRIVATE PRACTICE

Mental conditioning also requires recognizing a continuity of purpose in all your dealings with patients. The impact of any case presentation is heightened or hampered in the context of all past events patients have experienced, as well as the anticipation of all future events. The experiences you offer patients will perpetuate a psychological ripple effect throughout all of dentistry. Your treatment plan may occur at the beginning, middle, or end of the line of experiences patients need before they're ready to accept complete dentistry. Rather than becoming discouraged when patients refuse comprehensive care, think of your recommendations as an important step to patients' eventual acceptance. Your influence may make them ready to accept care the next time it's offered, no matter who makes the recommendation. Seeing yourself on a continuum of care is essential for a healthy dental practice. There's really no such thing as a "private" practice.

Appreciate your role in the delivery of dental care. Extend your horizons beyond those events that happen in your dental chair. You may never know the impact you've had on patients who have heard your treatment recommendations. Like the size of the rock thrown into the water, your ripples of influence will extend only as far as the weight of your commitment and the scope of your vision.

HOW TO CONSISTENTLY DELIVER VALUE

Much of what this book is about is providing value. Again, value is the relationship between what patients receive in contrast to what they pay (give) for it. Value is relative worth. Experiencing value means getting your money's worth and a little bit more. In Chapter 5 I discussed how providing value is the key to differentiating yourself in the mind of the patient. Patients have a hard time differentiating us based on the objective clinical quality of our care. Differentiating us based on service and relative value, however, is easy.

In every preceding chapter I've emphasized opportunities and techniques to provide value. The opportunities to provide value are nearly infinite. Whenever there is an opportunity for service, there is a way of sweetening that service with a pinch of value. The techniques for providing value are also nearly limitless. Techniques can vary, depending on the needs of the patient (a valuable service to one patient may not be valuable to another) and on the talents of the provider. Interest and imagination provide the incubator of great ideas for seeing and providing great value.

The Achilles' heel of providing great value is consistency. Great value encourages the patient to expect more of the same. You know how it is; some days are better than others. Nothing is worse than being disappointed when you are expecting a great value experience and receive no value, or worse yet, a devaluing experience. Think about it. Have you ever been disappointed when dining at one of your favorite restaurants? You expected value and didn't receive it. How many times has this happened in your dental office? Patients who needed to experience value the most got the short end of the value stick?

Inconsistency when providing high value is much worse than consistently providing average value. High value creates an appetite that you better be able to satisfy. If you don't, you draw attention to the weakest links in your office. For example, perhaps you have an outstanding receptionist who can solve any problem. Patients value her because she's completely in control of what she does and people like her. That's the good news. The bad news is no one is cross-trained in her job. When she is sick or changes jobs, it becomes obvious to patients where your weaknesses are.

A high value for many patients is experiencing a good-natured cheerfulness from the doctor and staff. Everyone loves a great chairside manner. Eliminate it for an appointment or two and watch and listen to reactions from your patients. Assistants will hear, "Is the doctor in a good mood today?" or, "Is everything going all right?" or, "Is there a problem with the doctor? He seems different." The biggest problems with a great chairside manner appear on the days when it's absent.

How do we create consistent value for our patients when as dentists and staff members we are subjected to an endless flow of stressors and challenges that treating the general public invites? How do we smile and dull the sharp edges of the day-to-day hassles and consistently look for opportunities to provide value? The answer is hidden in our inner motives. Do we seek to provide value because we want and expect people to reciprocate? I provide you value, you provide me value. This approach seems logical. It's what the win-win cliches are all about. "If I give my patients what they want, they'll give me what I want" is a common slogan. If you focus long and hard on what your patients want, surely you'll get what you want.

Let me ask you something: Have you ever busted your behind for a patient, given him or her outstanding service, and a great clinical result, and been deeply disappointed in the response? Have you ever gone the extra mile to support a staff member who needed your help, only to have that staff member act like you were his or her enemy? How about your relationship with your collegues? Have you ever been deeply disappointed in the actions of another dentist you thought was your friend?

We have all experienced great disappointments in relationships, in which we expected others' behavior toward us to be positively influenced by our prior positive behavior toward them. It seems there is only a loose inconsistent relationship between giving value and receiving it in return. When we receive it, we label it as "win-win." When we don't, we label it as "suffering."

To consistently provide value, let me suggest that we get rid of the win-win, tit-for-tat orientation. If our motive for providing value is conditional to the response we receive, we are building a major flaw into our orientation for providing value. We will never experience consistent reinforcement for providing value if that reinforcement is based on people doing nice things in return. Suffering and frustration is the result. The line of dentists would extend out of sight if there was a course, technique, or incentive system that guarantees if you do nice things for others, they'll do nice things for you.

To consistently provide value, we must uncouple the motive for providing value from the response of the recipient of that value. Providing value must become its own motive. To do so consistently, it needs to be unconditional. No conditions or expectations means no suffering or frustration. I'm not arguing against preferences. Of course, we would prefer people respond to our efforts. Just don't make your preference your sole motive.

Unconditional motives for providing value are not crippled by nonreciprocating responses, hence, consistency is unaffected. Inconsistency in providing value is the child of disappointments from previous experiences. You may ask, "Why should I focus on value? Most of my patients hate coming here anyway." Or, if you're a staff member, you may say, "This patient has always been a problem. I'm not going out of my way for her."

The reason to provide consistent value is that it's good for you. It's good for you to see what dentistry is beyond the technical and clinical aspects. Providing value is expressing the love for what you do and who you are. Being willing to provide value for no reason is the highest level of excellent service. When I decided to work and provide value for the unconditional love of it, most of my day-to-day frustrations disappeared. It's also been my experience that when I provided value unconditionally, my staff followed my example. Consistently providing unconditional value is the heart of the issue of selling reconstructive dentistry.

The no-contest case presentation style is the framework onto which unconditional value is built. With this attitude, you and your staff will break through the barriers to reconstructive dentistry and experience greater self-fulfillment and prosperity.

Epilogue

Are dentists an endangered species? No more so than any other professional, business person, teacher, or laborer. Thriving in the marketplace has always meant keeping your head out of the sand, anticipating change and capturing opportunities. The changing business environment will force some dentists out and make others stronger. Which one it will be for you will depend on how you anticipate and adapt to change.

The business climate always changes. Somehow health care professionals have thought they're immune to the sometimes upsetting realities of the marketplace. I've often thought the prefix "Dr." in front of our names created the illusion of having a "bullet proof" lifestyle. It doesn't. Once that realization hits home, then you are on the way to adapting your practice to coincide with the demands of the business climate.

We cannot change the world. We must change ourselves. This book is about changing ourselves. It emphasizes case presentation as a starting point for preserving fee-for-service care. Why? Because our ability to sell our services, regardless of the business climate, will be the distinguishing characteristic between dentists who make it and those who don't.

To change means to grow. Growth has always been the foundation of success. Success is the fragrance of growth. Who we become on the road to success is the fruit of our labor. The struggle to preserve fee-for-service dentistry will be our teacher. It will teach us how to provide more value. It will teach us how to build stronger relationships. It will teach us how to become wealthy. It will teach us how to grow wise. The best reason for success in dentistry is who we have to become to accomplish it.

Dr. Paul Homoly
January 26, 1996

Give the Gift of this Survival Strategy to Your Friends and Colleagues

Dr. Paul Homoly offers a one-day seminar, *Dentists: An Endangered Species–practical strategies for fee-for-service care.* This seminar is for the entire dental team and offers what every fee-for-service dentist wants–a practice model that will endure in the changing business climate, how to provide care outside the limitations of dental insurance, enjoy a predictable collections policy, how to take the stress out of selling and practice philosophy that makes a career in dentistry survivable.

Additionally, Dr. Paul Homoly offers *The MasterMind Curriculum: for prosperity and preserving fee-for-service dentistry.*

The MasterMind Curriculum is *not* a course or a study club. It's a group of like-minded dentists, who together with their staffs, create relationships that focus on cooperative prosperity.

Cooperative prosperity is a process where we discover the leverage of success oriented dentists participating in each other's success. Borrowing the concept from the real estate, insurance and marketing industries, cooperative prosperity in effect puts the most successful practitioners on your side. We'll discover how we each hold part of the pieces to one another's success puzzle.

In its complete form, there are six one-day *MasterMind Curriculum* sessions given every other month over the period of a year.

For more information about these live and audio cassette programs call Dr. Paul Homoly **(704) 527-6600** or e-mail **phomoly@aol.com.**